Our Debt to Greece and Rome

EDITORS
GEORGE DEPUE HADZSITS, PH.D.

DAVID MOORE ROBINSON, PH.D., LL.D.

MATHEMATICS

BY
DAVID EUGENE SMITH
PROFESSOR OF MATHEMATICS

INTRODUCTION BY
SIR THOMAS LITTLE HEATH

COOPER SQUARE PUBLISHERS, INC.
NEW YORK
1963

Published 1963 by Cooper Square Publishers, Inc.
59 Fourth Avenue, New York 3, N. Y.
Library of Congress Catalog Card No. 63-10294

INTRODUCTION

THE history of the beginnings of mathematics in the sense in which we understand the term is the history of mathematics in Greece; for it was the Greeks who first conceived the notion of mathematics as a science in and for itself, and it was they who established mathematics as a logical system based upon a few elementary principles, principles which they were the first to lay down and which remain substantially unshaken to the present day.

If it is true that any one who desires to get to the root of a subject should study it historically, it should seem almost superfluous to urge the student of mathematics to go to the sources. But it is not only the mathematician who should study the original works of the Greek masters. Some acquaintance with them is necessary to any one who would understand the Greek genius in all its many-sided aspects and in some sort feel the inspiration which all succeeding ages

[v]

have drawn from the imperishable monuments which it has left us. For the mathematics of the Greeks was on a level with their pioneer work in all the other intellectual pursuits, literature, philosophy, art and science, which make life worth living to a rational human being. In their mathematics we see the same untrammelled intellectual freedom, the same truthfulness and directness, that characterize their work in other fields, and even the same love of beauty. Aristotle, for instance, expressly combats the view that mathematics has nothing to do with beauty and the good; on the contrary, he says, what could be more beautiful than the order, symmetry and definiteness which mathematics exhibits in a very special degree?

The use of mathematics, in the view of the great Greek teachers, was to train the mind and to enable the soul to get a glimpse of truth; its practical application to everyday problems was of no account in comparison. In the *Republic* of Plato Socrates rallies Glaucon for thinking well of astronomy because it enables us to observe seasons, months and years. "You amuse me," he says, "by your evident alarm that the multitude should think that you insist upon useless studies. Yet indeed it *is* no easy matter, but on the contrary a very difficult one, to believe that in the midst of these studies an organ of our souls is being purged from the blindness, and quickened from the deadness, occasioned by other pursuits, — an organ the preservation of which is of more importance than a thousand eyes; because only by it can truth be seen. Consequently those who think with us will bestow unqualified approbation on the studies you prescribe, while those who have no inkling at all of this doctrine, will think them valueless, because they see no considerable advantage to be gained from them beyond their practical applications."

Archimedes, again, whose clever mechanical inventions, like the screw for pumping water and the engines of war which kept the Romans so long at bay when besieging Syracuse, had (as Plutarch relates) brought him the reputation of more than human wisdom, thought nothing of such things; nay, he regarded as ignoble and sordid the business of mechanics and every sort of art that is directed to use and profit, and placed his whole ambition in these speculations, the beauty and subtlety of which is untainted by any admixture of the common needs of life. In this spirit it was that he ordered to be engraved on his tomb a representation of a cylinder and a sphere inscribed in it, with the ratio (3 : 2) of their surfaces and volumes which he had discovered.

And may we not claim that today, in the welter of things resulting from the Great War, it should do every one good to turn aside and breathe for a while the pure atmosphere of abstract thought which we find in Greek mathematics, that "independent world," as Wordsworth eloquently called it, "created out of pure intelligence"?

Indeed there could not be a more appropriate time for the appearance of a Series such as that of which the present volume forms a part.

THOMAS LITTLE HEATH

LONDON, JANUARY 1923.

[viii]

CONTENTS

[ix]

CONTENTS

[x]

MATHEMATICS

MATHEMATICS

I. PRELIMINARY SURVEY

1. Leading Contributions of Greece

General Debt to Greece. If a man of scholarly tastes, even though gifted with only moderate intelligence, were asked where one should seek the ancient home of philosophy, he would wonder at the motive that could prompt a question upon which the opinion of the world is so unanimous. If the architect were asked a similar question with respect to his chosen field of labor, he too would marvel how a man of even modest attainments could have cause for doubt as to the answer. And so we might run the gamut of intellectual pursuits; of the graphic and plastic arts; of dramatic, musical, and forensic expression; of politics, and of all that makes for the higher life, and the answer would be the same, — the culmination of each in ancient times is found in the Greek civilization.

Precisely wherein lay the secrets of this power of Greece? Sir Thomas Heath, than whom no one is more conversant with her mathematical ideals, in an address upon *Greek Mathematics and Science*, has thus summarized the special aptitudes which her scholars possessed for success in these fields:

"They had, first, a love of knowledge for its own sake amounting, as Butcher says, to an instinct and a passion; secondly, a love of truth and a determination to see things as they are; thirdly, a remarkable capacity for accurate observation. Fourthly, while eagerly assimilating information from all quarters, from Egypt and Babylon in particular, they had an unerring instinct for taking what was worth having and rejecting the rest. As one writer has said, 'It remains their everlasting glory that they discovered and made use of the serious scientific elements in the confused and complex mass of exact observations and superstitious ideas which constituted the priestly wisdom of the East and threw all the fantastic rubbish on one side.' Fifthly, they possessed a speculative genius unrivalled in the world's history.

"It was this unique combination of gifts which

[2]

qualified the Greeks to lead the world in all the intellectual pursuits that make life worth living.

"Last, but not less important, the Greeks possessed the advantage over the Egyptians and Babylonians of having no priesthood which could monopolize learning as a preserve of its own, with the inevitable result of sterilizing it by keeping it bound up with religious dogmas and prescribed and narrow routine."

Special Debt of Mathematics. In view of these aptitudes of the Greeks, it is not to be wondered that the mathematician, — whose thought is so closely allied to the speculations of the philosopher, and whose domain of interest once included music and astronomy, and who not infrequently offered a helping hand to all the various fine arts, — should likewise claim Greece for the birthplace of his own chosen science.

Whether the peculiar traits of the Hellenic mind already mentioned were sufficient to account for the most logical number theory, for example, that was known in ancient times, while Greece in the same period was developing the most graceful dance of all the ages, is a further question for the philosopher; but the fact is patent, and it is now

[3]

proposed to accept that fact for the time being, and to consider some of the larger features of Greek mathematics, discussing later the details which they included.

Mathematics is a term that is loosely used at present to cover various subjects which, except by tradition, are not always closely related. We speak of arithmetic as one of these subjects, but the term has a different meaning from that ascribed to it by the classical writers, and its present connection with demonstrative geometry, for example, is nearly negligible. Music has not been considered a part of mathematics for some four centuries, although for at least two thousand years it was so looked upon in all of Western Europe. The name of algebra is comparatively modern, and the subject as today conceived was almost unknown to the Greeks. Hence it might seem that, after all, the roots of the science as we understand it must be sought elsewhere than in Athens, Alexandria, and the Aegean Islands. This, however, is not the case, and we shall presently see that each of the several branches sprang from the sturdy trunk of Greek *mathesis*.

[4]

Pre-Grecian Mathematics. It is quite evident, however, that mathematics existed before the Grecian civilization was born, and that the Greeks derived much knowledge of the subject from Egypt and Babylon, possibly from Crete, and possibly also from India and China, — but none of this was what we know as the distinctively Greek mathematics, and little of it represents the mathematical disciplines as we now recognize them. Before the seventh century B.C., which is the period of the birth of the science in Ionia, Egypt had contributed a rather crude system of numerals, no worse and but little better than various others of the early races. She had done something with unit fractions (fractions like $\frac{1}{4}$, with the numerator unity) and had also contributed a few number puzzles which we would now solve by algebra, but which her own scholars solved by trial. Her engineers had shown great skill in running levels and in establishing planes with a given gradient, and her *harpedonaptae* ("rope-stretchers," surveyors) had developed certain convenient rules in their useful craft.

The scientists of Mesopotamia, chiefly

astrologers, no doubt, had developed a cumbersome system of numerals and had prepared elaborate sets of tables of products, powers, quotients, and roots; and they, like the Egyptians, had made a slight advance in the study of fractions. Like the Egyptians also, they had developed a few simple rules of mensuration, and had made a few applications of their mathematics to a primitive type of astronomy.

The history of ancient India is almost completely sealed to us. We have the Mahabhārata, the Rāmayāna, and the Vedic literature; but from none of these sources do we obtain any information of value relating to the early mathematics of her people. China offers a better field for study, but all that her pre-Grecian period has to offer is possibly (for the texts may have been considerably corrupted) a few records of eclipses and a certain number of interesting rules and puzzles in mensuration.

In the eastern littoral region of the Mediterranean, where the trade from the Orient branched towards Egypt on the south and the distributing centers of Asia Minor on the north, there developed, so tradition says,

[6]

a fairly elaborate commercial arithmetic. This is quite reasonable of belief, since the same was true of the country watered by the Tigris and the Euphrates. Indeed, the early home of this humble type of mathematics may very likely have been located in Mesopotamia instead of Phœnicia.

So we find that, long before the warlike Dorians had established their dominion in Peloponnesus, computation, mensuration, and, no doubt, considerable number mysticism were known in various parts of the ancient world.

General Nature of the Greek Contribution. What, then, were the mathematical contributions peculiar to the Greeks? Did these people simply accept the accumulated wisdom of the past and add to it their more mature quota of knowledge, or were they able to contribute to the world something that was new, becoming creators instead of mere transmitters?

The answer is very simple and very direct: Within four centuries after Thales (*c.* 575 B.C.) founded the Ionian School of philosophy, there had developed in the Greek civilization an entirely new type of mathematics,

[7]

based upon new principles, and having new aims and new methods. It is in this epoch-making advance that all subsequent mathematics finds its beginning, and to this beginning the world is largely indebted for the basal principles upon which rests our present science of number, form, and space. In particular, we shall find that it was in these centuries that the foundations were laid for our modern theory of numbers, for our elementary geometry, for the study of conics and higher plane curves, for mathematical mechanics, and even, though more remotely, for the integral calculus. There have been numerous epoch-making periods in the history of mathematics, but considering all the circumstances and results, it is certain that there has never been a more significant one than that which included the names of Thales, Pythagoras, Eudoxus, Plato, Aristotle, Euclid, Apollonius, and Archimedes.

The three centuries that followed the death (*c.* 501 B.C.) of Pythagoras saw the foundations laid for geometry as a logical science, saw written the greatest textbook of the world, the *Elements* of Euclid, and saw mechanics placed upon a mathematical basis, infinite and higher series added to the mathematical store; conic sections then reached its highest point in ancient times, algebra approached the scientific stage, higher plane curves were made a subject of investigation, and the best number system of the pre-Christian world was developed and brought into use; and all this was done through the intellectual prowess of Greek scholars.

This is, however, by no means the complete record of their achievements in the field of mathematics, and we shall presently find that to them are also due the first steps of great significance in trigonometry, in geodesy, and in the application of mathematics to such physical problems as their scientists had at that time developed.

2. LEADING CONTRIBUTIONS OF ROME

Roman Ideals. It is a mere commonplace to say that the mind of Rome was radically different from the mind of Greece, and wherein that difference lay is set forth in the appropriate volumes in this series. Indebted to Greece for her initial inspiration, Rome also produced a noble and a notable

literature; indebted to Greece for the oratory
of Demosthenes, she produced a Cicero;
indebted as she also was to others for her
knowledge of politics, arms, and law, she nevertheless led the world in practical politics
and in military affairs and established a code
of laws that still influences jurisprudence
today; but indebted to Greece as she was
for an opportunity to develop pure mathematics, she produced not a single mathematician of the first rank, nor did she produce
a single treatise on this branch of the subject
that showed the slightest originality. Her
roll of scholars includes such names as Varro,
P. Nigidius Figulus, Vitruvius, Frontinus,
Hyginus, Balbus, Domitius Ulpianus, and
Nipsus, but no one of these men appreciated
the mathematics of Euclid, and far less that
of Archimedes and Apollonius. Cicero felt
this fact so keenly that he was moved to express his regret over the attitude of the Latin
mind, in these words:[1]

In summo apud illos [*i.e.*, Graecos] honore
geometria fuit; itaque nihil mathematicis inlus-
trius. At nos metiendi ratiocinandique utilitate
huius artis terminavimus modum.

"Geometry was in high esteem with them [*i.e.*, the Greeks], therefore none were more honorable than mathematicians. But we have confined this art to bare measuring and calculating."

Mathematics of Rome. It must not be felt, however, that Rome had no use for mathematics; indeed, she made a more tangible use of it than the Greeks, and this is precisely where one of the marked differences in the mental attitude of the two peoples shows itself. Greece was concerned chiefly with developing the mind of man, in fashioning his immortal soul; Rome, in exalting the power of the State, gave her attention to developing a great military and commercial commonwealth.

Hence Rome developed not the pure mathematics, as it is called, but the applied side of the science. She needed wholesome water for the health of her people, and she applied mathematics to the construction of her great aqueducts. She needed to lay out camps for her soldiers, and new cities in her recently acquired lands, and the artistic was subordinated to the practical in the rectangular crossing of thoroughfares. Hence the science of surveying, learned in part, no doubt, from the Egyptians, reached the highest stage in all antiquity at the hands of her *agrimensores* (literally, "field-measurers").

Thus the Greeks may be said to have developed to the highest degree the theory of mathematics, with relatively little attention to its practical applications; and the Romans may be said to have developed to the highest degree the commercial applications of the science, with relatively little attention to the theory. For the symmetric development of mathematics as a whole, each people was the complement of the other, and together they furnished the world with the bases for all future development.

Our general knowledge of mathematics today is vastly greater than that possessed by any scholar, however brilliant, who lived before the seventeenth century, and hence it is far superior to that of Pythagoras, Archimedes, Euclid, Apollonius, Diophantus, or any other of those men of genius who made the science of the classical period. On the other hand, it will be clear to anyone who conscientiously investigates the matter that modern mathematics could never have reached its present height had it not been built upon the foundations laid by the Greeks and, of another type, by the Romans. If its devotees had relied only upon the knowledge inherited from Egypt, from Babylon, from the Far East, or even from Rome alone, they could neither contemplate the science of to-day with the pardonable satisfaction which they now experience, nor look with their present confidence to still more significant achievements in the future.

It is for the purpose of fairly weighing the debt that we owe to Greece, and to a less degree our debt to Rome, in the field of mathematics, that this little study has been made.

II. THE CONTRIBUTIONS IN DETAIL

1. LOGISTIC

Two-fold Nature of Arithmetic. We commonly give the name "arithmetic" to that part of mathematics which treats primarily of numerical relations, taking the name from the Greek word for number (ἀριθμός, *arithmos*). The ancients, however, used the term to denote only the theory of numbers,—such as the study of primes, or the properties of square numbers. To the practical use of numbers, including the methods of writing them and of computing with them, they gave the name "logistic" (λογιστική, *logistike;* in Latin, *logistica*). This was looked upon by ancient scholars as a somewhat plebeian art, while arithmetic was considered an intellectual pursuit worthy of the attention of the philosopher. Plato possibly refers to this dual nature of the work with numbers when he says: "Arithmetic is of two kinds, one of which is popular, and the other philosophical." [2]

[14]

Because of its non-intellectual nature, logistic was not ranked as one of the four mathematical sciences; it was part of the trade of a commercial apprentice; it had no serious advocacy in the schools of philosophy; so humble was its status that it was taught chiefly by slaves, and not a single treatise on the subject has come down to us from classical times. We have no idea how Plato divided one number of any size by another; indeed, we have no direct evidence that he could perform the operation at all. It is probable that people looked upon the use of numbers, in a topic like division (at that time a very difficult art), in much the same way that we look upon it in connection with the slide rule or the calculating machine, — as a technicality of trade.

Greek Notation of the Classical Period. In order to perform such operations as addition, subtraction, multiplication, and division, it is necessary to have a system of notation, and here was one of the chief stumbling-blocks of ancient mathematics. With the limitations imposed by the paucity of writing materials, the Sumerians, and later the Babylonians (using the term to include the ancient inhabitants of Assur, who gave their name to Assyria, and the descendants of the Kaldi, who later created the Chaldean empire), worked out a system of numerals that served fairly well for writing but was of no value in computation.

The Egyptians, having in their papyrus a better medium for recording their ideas, developed a more satisfactory system of writing and a more usable set of numerals, although these numerals, like those of Babylon, were of little value for certain kinds of computation.

The Greeks began with a system that was no better than the others of early times, but later they made a marked improvement upon all of these systems, and finally devised the best one of the entire pre-Christian period. Whereas the ancient world, recognizing the ten fingers as offering a convenient base for counting, had generally repeated each numeral character up to nine units (as in the case of IIIIIIIII for nine, with various groupings), the Greeks of the classical period made use of five units, five tens, and five hundreds in order to make it easier to read their numbers. They took Π (from πέντε, *pente;*

[16]

the letter being written in the old form, with the right vertical line shorter than the left) for five, Δ (from δέκα, *deka*) for ten, and Η (from the old Attic breathing in ἑκατόν, *hekaton*) for hundred. They then wrote a small Δ inside the Π for five tens, or fifty; and a small Η inside the Π for five hundreds. They could thus write ΗΗΔΔΔΠΙΙΙ for 238 and avoid using eight single strokes at the end, as the Egyptians and Babylonians were compelled to do.

Roman Notation. The Romans copied the Greek plan, with different forms for the numerals, and in later times would have written the number 238 as CCXXXVIII. Both the Greeks and Romans, therefore, recognized the value of a system in which no numeral need be used more than four times, although it might be repeated more often if desired, as in the common use of numerals like CICCCCCCVIIII for 1509 in the early years of the sixteenth century.

The various changes in these numerals, from the time of their first appearance until they were superseded for practical purposes by other systems, is an interesting study; but to treat of the subject with any approach to completeness would alone require a book of considerable size. Suffice it to say that each of the two systems answered the ancient needs so long as the computations were confined to the most common of the operations, that is, to addition and subtraction. If, for example, we attempt to add the following numbers, the one set being written in our common numerals and the other in the Roman numerals of the early Christian era, we find that, although it takes longer to write the latter forms, they are rather easier to add:

689	DC	LXXX	VIIII
797	DCC	LXXXXVII	
865	DCCCLX		V
2351	MMCCCL		I

The reason why the Roman is the easier for this purpose is that we need to learn an addition table if we are to add 9, 7, and 5; whereas, on the Roman system, we simply see that there are six I's, or VI; that there are then four V's, which are equal to two X's; that there are now ten X's, which are together equal to two L's; that there are now five L's, which are together equal to two C's and one L, and so on; in other words, we

[18]

need no addition table whatever. If, therefore, the work were confined to addition and
subtraction, the Greek or the Roman boy
would have had an easier time than a boy of
today, his only handicap being that it would
take him longer to write the numerals, — a
matter of relatively little moment in the
period in which he lived. This accounts in
part for the fact that, for purposes of bookkeeping, the Roman system maintained its
supremacy in certain parts of Europe for
fully five centuries after the modern (Hindu-
Arabic) system was introduced into Spain and
Italy.

When, however, it came to multiplication
and division, the problem was more complicated, and neither the Greek nor the Roman
numerals, of the types above described, met
the need in a satisfactory manner. Computers were therefore compelled to resort,
very likely in all cases of any difficulty, to
mechanical aids, some of which will be described in Chapter III.

Later Greek Notation. The later Greek
computers, beginning about the third century B.C., recognized the inefficiency of the
numeral system then in common use and

therefore devised one of more scientific merit, although it proved to be a less popular type. Adding to their alphabet three ancient letters so as to give them the twenty-seven characters needed for the purpose, they used the first nine of these letters to represent units, the second nine to represent tens, and the third nine to represent hundreds. They distinguished numerical combinations from words, when necessary, by placing a bar over them. If they wished to represent thousands, they again used the same symbols but placed a slanting line at the left. Thus, the units were represented by A, B, Γ, Δ, E, F, Z, H, Θ, the tens by I, K, Λ, M, N, Ξ, O, Π, φ, the hundreds by P, Ϛ, T, Y, Φ, X, Ψ, Ω, Λ, the thousands by /A, /B, /Γ, . . . and so on, the three ancient letters being used for six, ninety, and nine hundred. The ten thousands (μύριοι, *myrioi* or *murioi*) were represented by such forms as M for 10,000; $\overset{B}{M}$, for 20,000; $\overset{Γ}{M}$, for 30,000, and so on. In modern works, small letters are commonly used, thus: *α′* for A, *β* for B, . . ., and *,α* for /A, *,β* for /B. . . .

The following cases will serve to illustrate

[20]

the method of representing numbers in the Greek system in use at the beginning of our era :

$$\Lambda \Theta = 39 \qquad\qquad /B = 2000$$
$$PK\Delta = 124 \qquad\qquad /BK = 2020$$
$$\Phi Z = 507 \qquad\qquad /Z E \Xi H = 7268$$

This plan had one advantage over our modern numerals; it reduced the number of symbols used in writing a given number. On the other hand, it required the memorizing of the numerical values of twenty-seven different letters, a task that naturally rendered it unpopular.

This alphabetic principle was also adopted by the Hebrews, the method being well established in the second century B.C. The results were the same as in Greece, namely, that the system was reserved for the élite, the mass of people preferring the more simple methods used in earlier times. Nevertheless the step was in the direction of our modern system, — not in the form of the numerals, but in having a separate character for each of the nine units. The plan missed, however, the idea of place value, wherein the complete numerical significance of a character is determined by the place that it occupies, as in the case of 22, where the right-hand 2 denotes two units, and the left-hand 2 denotes two tens. It is this idea of place value that characterizes the system which we use and which requires some kind of a character to represent zero. Although there are a few slight traces of the idea of place value in various ancient systems of notation, including the Babylonian, Greek, and Roman, it never became significant until the zero, used in computations as at present, was introduced. This important event seems to have taken place in India at least as early as the eighth century.

Possible Greek Methods of Computing. The later Greek numerals were fairly well adapted to multiplication, and could even have been used with some facility in division. For example, consider the case of 24 times 37, using our numerals and those of the Greeks :

37	ΛΖ
24	ΚΔ
148	ΡΜΗ
74	ΨΜ
888	ΩΠΗ

The two processes are substantially alike in difficulty, except that the Greek notation has twenty-seven characters against our ten.

The reverse process of division might have been carried out quite as we do it; but we have no satisfactory record of how the Greeks or Romans who lived before the Christian era multiplied or divided, either with their numerals or by mechanical aids, although we find, in the works of Heron (probably in the first or second century) and of Eutocius (sixth century), some approach to the method shown above. We see, however, that the Greek numerals were sufficiently adapted to convenient computation to have been a step in the evolution which has culminated, for the present at least, in the system now in use.

Mechanical Aids. Not only were the numerals of the ancients ill adapted, in general, to elaborate calculation, but the absence of suitable writing materials rendered it difficult to perform even the simpler computations of addition and subtraction. Although papyrus had long been known in Egypt, it was not introduced into Grecian territory before the seventh century B.C.; parchment was not known before the fifth century B.C.; paper is a comparatively recent product, particularly in the cheaper grades; the clay tablets of the Babylonians and the wax tablets of the Romans were unsuited to computation; and the slate is a later product of Northern Europe.

The difficulty was met in various parts of the world by the invention of divers forms of the abacus. This name seemingly was derived from the Semitic *abq* (dust), referring to the fact that, in ancient times, a board covered with dust served somewhat the same purpose as the modern blackboard. This device was well known in the Greek and Roman schools, and Cicero speaks of Archimedes as having used it : [3]

Ex eadem urbe humilem homunculum a pulvere et radio excitabo, qui multis annis post fuit, Archimedem. Cuius ego quaestor ignoratum ab Syracusanis, cum esse omnino negarent, saeptum undique et vestitum vepribus et dumetis indagavi sepulcrum.

"I will summon up from his dust board and stylus a humble and obscure man of the same city, called Archimedes, who lived many years after; whose tomb, overgrown with shrubs and briers, I in my quaestorship discovered, although the Syracusans knew nothing of it, and even denied that there was any such thing remaining."

The Line Abacus. Some time before Plato, but in what part of the world or in what century is quite unknown, there developed one of the several types of line abacus. This form of abacus consists of a table upon which parallel lines are ruled, one to represent units, the next to represent tens, and so on. Upon these lines, or in the spaces between them, were placed objects to indicate the number of units, tens, hundreds, or other powers of ten that made up the number to be represented.

In ancient China the objects seem to have been sticks, for certain "counting stalks" are referred to as early as the fourth century B.C. These sticks are later spoken of as "bamboo rods," and a man of great wealth is referred to in the third century of our era as reckoning with ivory rods. Such computing sticks were later introduced into Japan, where they remained in common use until the sixteenth century (and for algebraic purposes until the nineteenth), and they were still used in Korea for computing purposes until about the time of the Japanese occupancy of the country.

In general, the ancients seem to have employed pebbles or, at a later time, small disks. These were loose pieces and were placed upon the lines as above stated or were fastened so as to slide on wires, on rods, or in grooves. The detailed method of computing with these instruments need not concern us, but it will later be shown that the influence of Greece and Rome upon subsequent mathematics is partly due to their having employed such devices and to the improvements which they made in the methods of using them.

The Abacus in Greece. The earliest definite references to what is apparently a line abacus are found in the works of certain Greek writers. Herodotus, speaking of the Egyptians, says that they "write their characters and reckon with pebbles, bringing the hand from right to left, while the Greeks go from left to right." This does not assign priority of invention to the Egyptians, but merely states that they went from right to left in their computations just as they commonly did in writing. No Egyptian or Babylonian abacus has come down to us, nor have we any description of the use of such a device. It would seem by what Herodotus says, however, that the lines of the Greek and Egyptian abaci ran vertically with respect to the operator.

As to the Greek instrument, we have a possible representation in the lower part of the Darius vase, a well-known specimen of the ceramic work of the classical period.[4] This represents either the table of a receiver of tribute or an abacus upon which he computes the income. We have also an abacus, of uncertain date, which was found on the island of Salamis in 1846 and which probably represents the form used by bankers. It is a slab of marble about 1.5 m. long and 0.75 m. wide, ruled by incised lines, and has characters to represent the talent, certain fractions of an obol, and the numbers 1, 5, 10, 50, 100, 500, 1000, and 5000.

Whether this form of ruled abacus is a Greek invention or was inherited from Egypt, Babylonia, or Phœnicia, we have at present no means of knowing. So far as we know from direct evidence, it is Greek.

The Roman Abacus. Rome undoubtedly inherited the line abacus from Greece, but she seems to have introduced the idea of a grooved table with beads so fastened to it as to allow them to be moved back and forth upon their respective lines. Rome also seems to have developed the idea of breaking each line, so that one part represented units of the order indicated, and the other part fives. For example, seven would be represented on the lowest line by one in the fives' portion and two in the units' portion. This form of the abacus was a relatively late invention, — perhaps, as occasionally asserted, of the second century.

There are numerous Latin references to the computing disks used upon the abacus, although none of them describes the abacus itself. In the following verses, for example, Juvenal refers to tablets used for actual computation, which could hardly have been other than those on which the disks were used: [5]

Computat et cevet. Ponatur calculus, adsint
Cum tabula pueri; numera sestertia quinque
Omnibus in rebus, numerentur deinde labores.

"He reckons up and still acts the wanton. Let us settle our accounts! Send for the slaves with my account book [tablets]. Reckon up five thousand sesterces in all! Then count up your services!"

Cicero speaks of the computing pieces as *aera*, showing that in his time they were made of brass; and Lucilius the satirist, who lived a little earlier, does the same, much as we speak of coppers and nickels instead of mentioning their monetary values.

The common name for the pieces, however, was *calculi*, — literally pebbles, or "marbles," being the diminutive plural of *calx* (limestone, of which marble is a species; from *calx* comes our word "chalk"). So we find Martial (II, 48) including among his modest wants *"tabulamque calculosque."* The pieces were also called *abaculi* and were made of glass as well as stone, and so Pliny remarks: [6]

Fragmenta teporata agglutinantur tamen; rursus tota fundi non queunt, praeterquam abrupta sibimet in guttas, veluti cum calculi fiunt, quos quidam abaculos appellant, aliquos etiam pluribus modis versicolores.

"When broken, too, glass admits of being joined by the agency of heat; but it cannot be wholly fused without being pulverized into small fragments [*in guttas*, as in the Bamberg MS.], as we see done in the process of making small chequers [*calculi*], known as 'abaculi,' for mosaic work; some of which are of variegated colours, and of different shapes."

The word *calculus* had simply been carried over from the Greek ψῆφος (*psephos*, pebble), and it finally and quite naturally came to refer to the computing disk. From it came the word *calculare*, to compute (calculate). Unless they were slaves, those who did the computing were known as *calculatores* or *numerarii*, literally "pebblers" or "coiners."

The disks used in playing such games as backgammon, or at least the *ludus latrunculorum* and the *ludus duodecim scriptorum* (the precise nature of neither of which is known), were also called *calculi*, and our poker chips and checkers are relics of these computing disks as they were used in the playing of games.

We shall presently see that the influence of the Greek and Roman abacus upon later methods of computation and upon the terminology employed was considerable.

Finger Notation. The idea of counting on the fingers is, of course, primitive. The hands, or sometimes the hands and feet, formed the world's first important abacus, but the idea of representing large numbers upon the hands is first referred to in Greek literature. Herodotus speaks of his countrymen as being familiar with it in the fifth century B.C. It is more frequently mentioned by Latin writers, apparently because it was chiefly a commercial device used by traders in the international fairs, where digital communication helped to overcome linguistic difficulties.

The Greeks and Romans developed a scheme by which the smaller numbers used in everyday life, namely, those to one hundred, could be represented by eighteen different positions of the fingers of the left hand. The numbers from a hundred to ten thousand were similarly represented by the right hand. The left hand, applied to different parts of the body, was used to express numbers from 10,000 to 90,000, and the right hand was similarly used for larger numbers. Macrobius speaks of a certain statue of Janus as

[31]

representing upon his hands the number of days of the year, the hundreds upon the right hand, the units and tens upon the left: [7]

Inde et simulacrum eius plerumque fingitur manu dextra CCC et sinistra sexaginta et quinque numerum tenens ad demonstrandum anni dimensionem.

"Commonly his statue is made, holding the number 300 upon the right hand, and 65 upon the left, for the purpose of showing the length of the year."

A further interesting illustration occurs in Juvenal, who says: [8]

Felix nimirum, qui tot per saecula mortem
Distulit atque suos jam dextra computat annos.

"Happy was he indeed who postponed the hour of his death so long, and finally numbers his years upon his right hand."

2. ARTIFICIAL NUMBERS

Common Fractions. Primitive man had little need for fractions of any kind. The integers (or so-called "natural numbers") to ten or twenty satisfied his simple needs.

He could break an object into parts, but until trade rendered it necessary to invent a name for these parts it is not likely that any term other than "broken" was needed. Such a term, once it appears in popular language, tends to persist, and this tendency is illustrated in our very word "fraction," derived, as it is, from the Latin *frangere*, to break. Thus there arose, in time, systems of numbers which did not belong to the "natural" type of integers, and which, for want of a better term, may be spoken of as "artificial."

When human needs came to require the naming of portions of an object, the race seems generally to have been long content with only such parts as $\frac{1}{2}$, $\frac{1}{3}$, $\frac{1}{4}$, $\frac{1}{8}$, and so on, the results being the unit fractions already mentioned. Such concepts are found in the early records of Babylon, in the Ahmes Papyrus of Egypt (*c.* 1550 B.C.), in the writings of Heron (*c.* 50, or possibly as late as 200), in an Egyptian manuscript of about the eighth century, in works as late as the European Renaissance, and in our diamond measure even today. The idea of a common fraction with a numerator other than unity

[33]

entered into the mathematics of the Golden Age of Babylon and Egypt, but it had little immediate influence.

Because of the difficulties encountered in dealing with fractions, the ancients created various systems of measure involving sub-units. For example, instead of speaking of $\frac{1}{3}$ of a yard (to use our terms), they gave to this fraction such a name as "foot," and instead of speaking of $\frac{2}{3}$ of a yard they could then speak of 2 feet. This simple plan was carried throughout all kinds of measures — length, area, volume, weight, value, time, and so on, and resulted in such compound numbers as 3 yd. 2 ft. 4 in., relics of antiquity that are now happily disappearing or are being reduced to a minimum.

The Romans were partial to twelve as a basis for their divisions of measures for the reason that this number, being divisible by 2, 3, 4, and 6, permits of the taking of simple fractional parts which themselves are integral. This advantage possessed by twelve was recognized by other early peoples, but it was chiefly the Romans who made use of it. They divided their foot into twelfths, each being called an *uncia* (twelfth), — a term which gave us our word "inch"; and they used the same fractional part (*uncia*) of a pound, whence we have also our word "ounce." They counted commercially by twelves, and their *duodecim* gave us our "dozen."

Although the Romans recognized various numbers of twelfths, they had no good notation for common fractions. Instead of speaking of a half, they used the word *semis*, and $\frac{1}{2}$ of an *as* was indicated by the initial S. Similarly, they spoke of $\frac{1}{3}$ as *triens*, often indicating it upon coins by four large dots (••••), each standing for *uncia*, the $\frac{4}{12}$ being equal to $\frac{1}{3}$. Their fraction names included one representing $\frac{1}{2}$ of $\frac{1}{12}$ of $\frac{1}{12}$, or $\frac{1}{288}$, namely, the *scriptulum*, *scripulum*, or *scrupulum*, from which we still have the "scruple" of our apothecary's weight, a word also used to mean anything small, such as a small doubt.

The Greeks and Romans were not, however, without means of representing fractions in their higher works on mathematics, for they brought to their aid the idea of ratio, and hence could speak of the ratio of a line that was fifteen units long to a line that was seventeen units long, although they had no convenient symbol for $\frac{15}{17}$.

The Greeks also used the system of sub-units, and it was from them that the Romans derived a portion of their fraction system. Their scientific needs being greater than those of the Romans, they made more progress toward the development of fractions. For example, Archimedes wrote the word for the numerator and the numerical symbol for the denominator, as if we should write "fifteen 17ths"; but Heron used a numeral in each case, duplicating it in the denominator, as if we should write 2′ 5″ 5″ for $\frac{2}{5}$. Diophantus wrote the numerator, then an abbreviation of μόριον (*morion*, part), and finally the denominator, as in ĪB̄ΜΟΡϚ̄ΚΔ for $\frac{12}{224}$. Ordinarily, however, the Greeks preferred to use unit fractions, as if we should write $\frac{1}{2} + \frac{1}{4} + \frac{1}{8} + \frac{1}{16}$ for $\frac{15}{16}$. In this particular case they wrote CΔ″H″IF″, a symbolism that was hardly more complex than the one mentioned above.

Sexagesimal Fractions. For scientific purposes the Greek astronomers perfected a system of fractions which had been suggested, but not commonly used, by the Babylonians.

Since the number of its factors permits of the easy expression of such parts as $\frac{1}{2}$, $\frac{1}{3}$, $\frac{1}{4}$, $\frac{1}{5}$, $\frac{1}{6}$, and $\frac{1}{12}$, these people showed a predilection for sixty. They even used it as a kind of numerical base in writing, 1 (expressed in the cuneiform character) standing for sixty as well as one, and 11 standing for sixty-one as well as two.

Because of the large number of factors of 120, the Greek astronomers took 120 units for the diameter of their standard circle, or 60 units for the radius. Making use of 3 as the value of π commonly used by ancient peoples, they were led to take 3 × 120, or 360, as the number of units in a circumference. Following the Babylonian suggestion, they divided each of these units into sixtieths, and these new units again into sixtieths, and so on. This circular unit the Greeks called a μοῖρα (moira, position or degree), a term which the Latins translated as *gradus* (step) and which appears in English as "degree." The sixtieth of a μοῖρα they called πρῶτα ἑξηκοστά (*prota hexekosta*) or λεπτά (*lepta*), a term which appeared in Latin as *pars minuta prima*. The next lower unit was the δεύτερα ἑξηκοστά (*deutera hexekosta;* Latin, *pars minuta secunda*), and so on. When these terms were translated into English they were abbreviated into "minute" and "second," although "prime" and "second" would have been more in harmony with the original. It is interesting to see that, although we speak of 32′ 45″ as " 32 minutes 45 seconds," we speak of A' B'' as "A-prime B-second."

These sexagesimal fractions derive their name from the Latin *sexagesimus* (sixtieth; from *sexaginta*, sixty), but in the Middle Ages they were commonly called physical or astronomical fractions. To distinguish these forms from those commonly used by merchants, the latter were known as *fractiones vulgares*, whence we have the "vulgar fractions" of England and the "common fractions" of America, — names which are likely to endure in spite of the fact that the decimal fraction, a late invention, is at present the most common of all the fractional types.

3. ARITHMETIC

The Arithmetica. The Greek ἀριθμητική (*arithmetike*) became the Latin *arithmetica,* the term being used, as already stated, to refer to the theory of numbers as distinguished from the art of calculation. How far back in human history the speculations on the mystic properties of numbers extend we have no means of knowing. Mankind needed but few numerals in the primitive stages of human development, just as our "contemporary ancestors," whom we find represented in various savage tribes today, have little need for counting. Barter, the early method of exchange of products, requires the recognition of only a few number names; and until the days of systematic taxation, say in the fourth or fifth millennium B.C., numbers of any size were probably not needed for practical purposes. Indeed, it was not until coins were introduced as a medium of exchange, about the seventh century B.C., that the mercantile class came to need the type of numerical problem that we have today. Before this time, however, the banking class had dealt in gold and silver by weight, had charged interest, and had issued bills of exchange; but for the great mass of people the numbers in use were undoubtedly very small, limited,

[39]

for thousands of years, to the ten which represented the number of fingers upon the two hands.

Mystery of Numbers. Among these ten numbers there are two of special interest. The even numbers, after the first one, were capable of separation into other numbers; they were therefore prolific and were considered as feminine and earthly. The odd numbers were therefore ranked as masculine and, in the days of masculine brute force, as divine. Two of these odd numbers (three and seven) were not connected, as five was, with the finger scheme, and for this reason, apparently, they were looked upon by primitive people as in a class by themselves, — mysterious, potent for good and evil, and particularly divine. This superstition, which includes the familiar one that "there is luck in odd numbers," is general, being confined to no country and to no epoch, although it is first definitely expressed in the Pythagorean literature. In such fanciful notions are to be found the beginnings of the ancient *arithmetica*, and these early ideas of the race were inherited by the Greeks and Romans from the prehistoric ages, precisely as they were inherited by other ancient peoples.

Nature of the Greek Theory of Numbers. While others simply accepted such beliefs, the classical writers developed them into something entirely apart from superstition. They searched into the general properties of numbers; they separated these numbers into digits (*digiti*, fingers), joints (*articuli*), and composites (*compositi*), — a relic of the early finger symbolism of the race; and they recognized the geometric forms connected with them, as illustrated by a square. In the figure here shown the unshaded part represents the number four, which is evidently, from the arrangement of the dots, the sum of one and three. The shaded part represents the number five, there being five dots in the five squares that form this portion of the figure. The Greek arithmeticians therefore saw that $1 + 3$ is equal to the square whose side is 2; that $1 + 3 + 5$ is equal to the square whose side is 3, and so on. In other words, they knew from the related geometric figure that the sum of the first n odd numbers is n^2.

In such a figure, an odd number like five can be represented by a kind of right angle, as here shown; the upright part resembles the pointer set up in a sundial and it was called a *gnomon* (γνῶμων; from γιγνώσκειν, γνῶναι, — *gignoskein, gnonai*, know), because the pointer casts a shadow by which we "know" the time of day and, indeed, the seasons as well. Therefore odd numbers were known as "gnomons."

From such sources there developed a more elaborate classification of numbers. Thus we find such terms as "even-times even numbers," which Euclid used for a number of the form 2^n; "even-times odd numbers," of the form $2(2n+1)$; and "odd-times odd numbers," of the form $(2m+1)(2n+1)$.

Besides square numbers the Greeks recognized other "polygonal numbers," such as triangular numbers, the latter being represented geometrically as follows:

It is apparent from these figures that the first triangular number (3) is equal to $1 + 2$;

[42]

that the next one (6) is equal to $1 + 2 + 3$; that the next one (10) is equal to $1 + 2 + 3 + 4$, and so on. In other words, a triangular number is simply the sum of the arithmetical series of the natural numbers beginning with unity, — a fact well known to the Greeks.

In a somewhat analogous manner the Greek scholars represented pentagonal numbers, hexagonal numbers, and so on. They also recognized oblong numbers, represented by a rectangle with unequal sides. For example, 3×4, or 12, is an oblong number or, as it was called, a heteromecic number. From the modern point of view a square (say 16) may also be a heteromecic number (2×8), and a heteromecic number may be a triangular number ($2 \times 5 = 10$) or both a triangular and a square number (36).

The Greeks also recognized solid numbers, the most common one being a cube. For example, if a cube has an edge equal to 3 linear units, the volume of the cube will contain $3 \times 3 \times 3$, or 27, cubic units, and hence the number 27, being thus related to the solid, was also called a cube. In a somewhat similar way the Greeks represented

pyramidal numbers, formed in general outline by piling spheres. For example, on
three spheres it is possible to place one
sphere to form the pyramidal number four.
It is in these numbers that we find the source
of the problems relating to the piling of
cannon balls, — problems still found in some
of our algebras.

When we consider triangular numbers,
square numbers, and cube numbers, we see
that 3 is the triangular root of 6, that it is
also the square root of 9 and the cube root
of 27, and that we might indefinitely extend
the idea of root to include such concepts as
roots of triangular pyramidal numbers. Out
of these various roots, with many of which
the Greeks were very likely familiar, we
have preserved in our mensuration only
the square root and the cube root, the reason being that these satisfy all our needs
in that domain. In algebra we follow the
Greeks in considering such roots as the fourth
and fifth, and our modern symbolism has
enabled us to extend the idea to include nth
roots in general, n being any kind of number.

This brief sketch will serve to show how
the Greeks joined their geometric forms to

their different types of number, why they gave geometric names to these types, and the method by which they developed certain rules which would now be expressed by algebraic symbols.

Contributions of the Pythagoreans. We are uncertain how far back these elementary ideas extend. Since Pythagoras (*c.* 572– *c.* 501 B.C.) was deeply interested in the number theory, it is thought that such ideas were taught in his school at Crotona, in Magna Graecia, a colony in Southern Italy. He was apparently the first to show that certain numbers (the square root of 2, for example) have no common measure with unity, — types which were later classified as incommensurable numbers. We have only tradition and general inference to aid us in our knowledge of the work of Pythagoras, but it seems fairly certain that he made use of geometry in establishing the property of incommensurability, and that he was familiar with the mean proportional between two lines or two numbers. He also seems to have been able to divide a line into two parts such that the rectangle contained by the whole line and one of the parts is equal to the square on the other part. Expressed algebraically, if a is the length of the line and x is one of the parts, then

$$ax = (a - x)^2$$
or $$x^2 - 3\,ax + a^2 = 0.$$

Since he could divide the line geometrically to meet these conditions, he could find a segment equal to x; in other words, he could solve the above quadratic equation geometrically.

Whether this knowledge can be attributed to Pythagoras himself, or even to his contemporaries, we cannot say, nor is it a matter of special moment in this discussion. Certain it is that the problem was solved by the Greeks in this general period of their development. There seems thus to have existed before the time of Plato an interesting number theory based upon geometry, although no contemporary treatises describing it have survived.

It is impossible to give the precise sources of much of this number theory, nor, as stated above, is it essential for our present purposes; but a few details will be given with the object of showing the general nature of the work. About this time, and possibly among the early Pythagoreans, there developed the idea of a "perfect number," that is, of a number that is equal to the sum of its aliquot parts (namely, of its factors, including unity). For example, six is a perfect number, because $6 = 1 + 2 + 3$, and 1, 2, and 3 are the aliquot parts of 6.

If the sum of the aliquot parts of a number is less than the number itself, as in the case of eight (where $1 + 2 + 4 < 8$), the number was said to be "deficient" (defective, elliptic). If, on the other hand, the sum of the aliquot parts exceeds the number as in the case of twelve (where $1 + 2 + 3 + 4 + 6 > 12$), the number was said to be "abundant" (redundant, superperfect).

It is also possible that the early Pythagoreans knew the class of numbers designated by the term "amicable." Two numbers were considered as amicable if each is equal to the sum of the aliquot parts of the other, as in the case of 220 and 284.

Euclid on Arithmetica. The first writer of any note to develop the number theory is one whose name is always thought of as a synonym for geometry, namely, Euclid of Alexandria (*c.* 300 B.C.). He was the world's first successful textbook maker in the field of mathematics; indeed, it is not too much to say that he is the most successful one who ever lived in any age, a statement that will be justified when we come, in the next chapter, to consider his influence. In six of the thirteen extant books of his *Elements* (Στοιχεῖα, *stoicheia*) he treats of the theory of numbers, of incommensurable magnitudes, and of such identities as would now be expressed by the algebraic formula

$$(a + b)^2 = a^2 + 2\,ab + b^2.$$

Some idea of the nature of the work may be obtained from two of Euclid's propositions. These may be stated in modern phraseology as follows: [9]

"If two numbers are prime to two other numbers, both to each, their products are also prime to one another."

"If an odd number is exactly contained in an even number, it is exactly contained in half that number."

[48]

Euclid also proved that if p is equal to $1 + 2 + 2^2 + \ldots + 2^n$ and is prime, $2^n p$ is a perfect number.

Eratosthenes and Archimedes. The next writer of consequence, in this field, was Eratosthenes ($c.$ 230 B.C.) — poet, librarian, friend of Archimedes, and one of the world's first great workers in the field of geodesy. His contribution to the number theory was limited, however, to a simple method, — that which relates to the finding of primes. He first considered the series of odd numbers, namely, 3, 5, 7, 9, 11, 13, 15, 17, 19, 21, ... From these he canceled the successive multiples of 3, then of 5, then of 7, then of 11, and so on, thus sifting out the non-primes. To this scheme he gave the name of "the sieve" (κόσκινον, *koskinon;* Latin, *cribrum*), and the method itself stands out as the oldest one known for the determination of a series of primes.

Archimedes ($c.$ 225 B.C.) had, as we shall see, other lines of mathematical interest, but he developed a scheme of counting by octads, that is, by the eighth power of ten, extending his number system as far as 10^{63} and making use of a law which would now be expressed by the algebraic identity $a^m a^n = a^{m+n}$.

Later Greek and Roman Arithmeticians. It was not until after the beginning of the Christian era that the effort was made by Greek writers to do for the *arithmetica* what Euclid had already done for elementary geometry and what Apollonius had done for conic sections, namely, to gather the accumulated knowledge on the subject and to incorporate it in a single treatise. The first attempt of any significance was made by Nicomachus (*c.* 100), not a mathematician of the first rank, who lived in Gerasa, not far from Jerusalem. In his work there appeared such propositions as that "every square, if increased by its own side, becomes a heteromecic number"; that is, to use our modern algebraic symbols, that $x^2 + x$ cannot be a square, but becomes an oblong. Nicomachus also showed that 6, 28, 496 and 8128 are perfect numbers.

About a quarter of a century later, Theon of Smyrna extended the theory by a number of propositions of the same general nature as those of Nicomachus, and with him there ended the notable contributions of the

Greeks to the subject, — except in the algebraic work of Diophantus, which will be mentioned later. Iamblichus (*c.* 325) added slightly to the theory, but the time had passed for Greek scholarship to assert itself.

Boëthius (480–524), a Roman who had studied in Athens, embodied in his *De Institutione Arithmetica Libri duo* much of the theory as set forth in the works of Euclid, Nicomachus, and Theon of Smyrna, but he added nothing that was original. Nevertheless, so superior was his work to that of any other writers of his period, and so superior was he to any other of the Latins who lived just after the Fall of Rome, that his arithmetic was looked upon by his degenerate countrymen as representing the highest type of scholarship. Moreover, his execution, brought about for political reasons, gave to the Church the opportunity of claiming him as a martyr, and hence his work dominated the teaching of the theory of numbers in all the schools of Christian Europe for a thousand years.

We shall see that the influence of this theory and that of Nicomachus and Theon of Smyrna was far more potent in the development of later mathematics than would at first seem probable.

4. ELEMENTARY GEOMETRY

Two Types of Elementary Geometry. The very etymology of the word "geometry" ($\gamma\hat{\eta}$ + $\mu\epsilon\tau\rho\epsilon\hat{\iota}\nu$, *ge* + *metrein*, to measure the earth) shows how far the science has departed from its primitive state. The subject was originally mensuration based upon simple intuition. In pre-Grecian times it reached its highest development in the work of the Egyptian and Babylonian surveyors, but it never advanced beyond the intuitive stage in which the measuring of tangible objects is the chief consideration.

This kind of mensuration, however, is entirely different from elementary geometry as conceived today. With us the purpose is primarily the logical demonstration of some particular truth concerning a given figure, — say a triangle, a circle, or a general polygon. This is the field of demonstrative geometry, and when confined to straight lines, polygons, and circles in a plane it constitutes what is known as elementary plane geometry. If we admit figures formed by several planes, or by certain curve surfaces, or by both, we thereby extend the work to include elementary solid geometry. The two constitute what we shall call elementary geometry.

Birth of Elementary Geometry. It is one of the greatest scientific contributions of the Greeks that they brought to light the subject of elementary geometry. Before the sixth century B.C., and in various parts of the earth, men had talked of squares and triangles and circles, and had used them in making measurements; but so far as the world knows, Thales of Miletus (*c.* 575 B.C.) was the first man who ever thought of scientifically demonstrating a proposition relating to such figures. He was apparently the first to conceive of the abstraction which we call a straight line, as distinct from a physical rod or wire or string, and hence to imagine the abstract forms which constitute the subject matter of elementary geometry. We do not know with certainty what propositions he demonstrated, nor do we know the method which he used in his proofs; for he left no writings of his own, and tradition is often born of mere inference. It is said that he discovered that a circle is bisected by any of its diameters, but this of itself would not have been an achievement to cause comment, since it is an intuitive fact that the world must have recognized for thousands of years. The only reason why it should have attracted any attention must be that, at last, it was definitely proved. To Thales is also attributed the proof that the angles at the base of an isosceles triangle are equal, that the vertically opposite angles formed by two intersecting lines are equal, and that two triangles are congruent if they have two angles and a side of one respectively equal to the corresponding parts of the other. He seems also to have inscribed a right-angled triangle in a circle, thus knowing, undoubtedly, that an angle inscribed in a semicircle is a right angle.

Such propositions are almost childish in content, but the proving of a single one of them was sufficient to lay the cornerstone for scientific mathematics. Geometry before the time of Thales may be characterized by the statement, "I see A and B";

geometry after his time, by the statement "If *A*, then *B*." The former was intuitive; the latter deductive.

The Makers of Elementary Geometry. Elementary geometry passed through three rather distinct periods in Greece: (1) The period of discovery, in which the followers of Pythagoras, himself a pupil of Thales, found many interesting facts in geometry and proved them in some kind of fashion; (2) the period of demonstration, in which Plato and his school laid down those bases of proof which developed into the axioms and postulates of later times, and also placed upon elementary geometry the restriction that only the ruler and compasses should be used in constructions; and (3) the period of exposition, in which various attempts were made by such minor writers as Leon (*c.* 375 B.C.) and Theudius (*c.* 360 B.C.) to set forth the theory in textbook form, — attempts that finally resulted in Euclid's *Elements* (*c.* 300 B.C.). This work embodied most of the pure mathematics, chiefly geometry, or geometry applied to the number theory, that had accumulated up to the time of the founding of the great School of Alexandria (*c.* 325 B.C.) by Ptolemy Soter.

Referring first to the immediate predecessors of Euclid, the commentary written by Proclus (*c.* 460 A.D.) mentions Euclid's indebtedness to those who had already written upon the subject, in these words:[10]

"Not much younger than these is Euclid, who put together the *Elements*, collecting many of the theorems of Eudoxus, perfecting many others by Theætetus, and bringing into irrefragable demonstration the propositions which had only been somewhat loosely proved by his predecessors."

It is of little moment who first proved any of the special propositions found in Euclid's geometry. As a matter of fact we know very little about this phase of mathematical history. We speak of Pythagoras, for example, as having proved that the square on the hypotenuse of a right-angled triangle is equal to the sum of the squares on the other two sides, but we have no convincing evidence upon the subject. No Greek writer connected the name of

Pythagoras directly with the proposition until centuries after the death of this great teacher. The geometric fact was already known in China and Egypt, at least for special cases, and possibly also in India and other countries, but the idea of proving it was purely Greek. Whether Pythagoras was the first to demonstrate the proposition will, so far as we can now see, always remain unknown, and for our immediate purposes it is unimportant.

The merits of Euclid's work were many; but some idea of its most distinctive features may be obtained from consideration of the fact that, up to his time, no one had shown any ability in writing a successful textbook. Euclid proceeded to group his propositions according to general content, devoting one book to the properties of rectilinear figures, one to circles, one to areas, and so on. He began by assuming a small number of generally accepted "common notions" (κοιναὶ ἔννοιαι, *koinai ennoiai*), — axioms, as we call them, — which everyone generally agrees are true; for example, he assumed that equals added to equals give results that are equal. He then "pe-

titioned" his hearers to allow him a few
geometric facts upon which he could base
his work, such as that a straight line can be
drawn from any point to any point. Such
a demand was called an αἴτημα (*aitema*,
demand; Latin, *petitio*), and later a *pos-
tulatum* (postulate). These postulates having been granted, Euclid was ready to
begin his logical solutions of problems and
his demonstrations of theorems. He de-
clined to consider a figure until he had
shown that and how it could be constructed,
and so he began with a simple problem, —
that of constructing an equilateral triangle.
His propositions then followed one another
in logical sequence until he had covered
the most important cases of elementary
geometry.

Perhaps the spirit of Euclid, and also
of Plato, can be most succinctly described
in the words of an anonymous reviewer
in *The Oxford Magazine* (March 6, 1913),
who is quoted with approval by Sir Thomas
Heath in the address already mentioned:

"To be a Greek was to seek to know; to
know the primordial substance of matter, to

know the meaning of number, to know the world as a rational whole. In no spirit of paradox one may say that Euclid is the most typical Greek: he would know to the bottom, and know as a rational system, the laws of the measurement of the earth. Plato, too, loved geometry and the wonders of numbers; he was essentially Greek, because he was essentially mathematical. It is true that he loved myths as well as mathematics; and it would be a long story to seek to show the affinities of the one with the other. But at any rate Plato sought to know and to understand; he demanded of every artist (be he craftsman or politician) a true knowledge of his art, and he demanded of every thinker that he should think things through and through to the Ideas which are their meaning. . . .

"And if one thus finds 'the Greek genius' in Euclid and in the *Posterior Analytics*, one will understand the motto written over the Academy —

μηδεὶς ἀγεωμέτρητος εἰσίτω *

"To know what the Greek genius meant, you must (if one may speak ἐν αἰνίγματι) begin

* *Medeis ageometretos eisito.* "Let no one ignorant of geometry enter here," — the world's first recorded college entrance requirement.

[59]

with geometry; and so beginning you may arrive at what the Greeks were always seeking — some knowledge of 'the question what being is,' and, incidentally, at some knowledge of the question what the 'being' of their genius was."

5. Higher Geometry

Nature of the Subject. When we speak of higher geometry among the Greeks we refer to that branch of mathematics which requires, in the construction of the geometric figures, other instruments than the compasses and the unmarked ruler. Such figures attracted the attention of the Greeks before Plato set his limitation upon elementary geometry. Hippias of Elis (*c.* 425 B.C.), for example, is thought to have invented the curve called the quadratrix, which was later studied by Deinostratus (*c.* 350 B.C.) and used for trisecting an angle and squaring a circle.

Conic Sections. The most important phase of higher geometry as studied by the Greeks is that relating to conic sections. There is a tradition, unsupported by satisfactory evidence, that these figures were first studied

by Menæchmus (*c.* 360 B.C.), a pupil of
Eudoxus (*c.* 370 B.C.) and a friend of Plato.
Mention is made by Eratosthenes (*c.* 230
B.C.) of certain "Menæchmian Triads,"
and it is thought that these were the conic
sections. It is also thought that he obtained them by taking sections of three
types of cone, each section being perpen-
dicular to an element. From the right-
angled cone the parabola was derived;
from the obtuse-angled cone, the hyperbola;
and from the acute-angled cone, the ellipse.

Although there is considerable doubt as
to whether Menæchmus wrote upon these
figures, it is certain that they were well
known about a century later. Archimedes
(*c.* 225 B.C.), for example, not only studied
the parabola, but also studied ellipsoids and
paraboloids of rotation, although he did not
use these particular names.

Of the writers on conics, Apollonius of
Perga (*c.* 225 B.C.) was the greatest in the
Greek period; indeed, all the circumstances
considered, he was the greatest of all time.
To him are due the terms "ellipse," "parabola," and "hyperbola," and to him is also
due the first textbook upon the subject.

This work consisted of eight books, the first four of which have been preserved to us in Greek manuscripts. The fifth, sixth, and seventh were translated into Arabic during the ascendancy of the caliphs of Bagdad, and from this source they were carried to the West. The eighth book is lost. In the first book Apollonius shows how all three conics can be produced from the same cone, instead, as in the Menæchmian tradition, from three cones of different shape. The first three books seem to have been largely compilations of the discoveries already made, but the others seem to have been the original work of Apollonius.

Thus the study of conic sections is purely Greek in origin, and the world's leading textbook on the subject, from the standpoint of the actual sections of a cone, is due to a Greek writer. Of the other inventions which had their influence upon analytic geometry mention will be made in the next chapter.

Higher Plane Curves. Not only did the Greeks begin and highly develop the study of conic sections, but they began and carried along with a considerable degree of success the more advanced study of plane curves, some of which we would now designate as of a degree higher than the second, and others of which were transcendental. One of these, the quadratrix, has already been mentioned as possibly due to Hippias of Elis. Among the others to be studied mathematically was the so-called Spiral of Archimedes, possibly suggested to the great Syracusan (for we have only tradition to depend upon) by his friend Conon, whom he knew when studying in Alexandria. Besides these lines there were others, such as those referred to by Proclus, whom Dr. Allman quotes as follows : [11]

"Nicomedes trisected every rectilineal angle by means of the conchoidal lines, the inventor of whose particular nature he is, and the origin, construction, and properties of which he has explained. Others have solved the same problem by means of the quadratrices of Hippias and Nicomedes, making use of the mixed lines which are called quadratrices; others, again, starting from the spirals of Archimedes, divided a rectilineal angle in a given ratio.

"In the same manner other mathematicians are accustomed to treat of curved lines, explaining the properties of each form. Thus, Apollonius shows the properties of each of the conic sections; Nicomedes those of the conchoids; Hippias those of the quadratrix, and Perseus those of the spirics."

Furthermore, Seneca tells us that Eudoxus, having in Egypt studied the motions of the planets, endeavored to explain them by means of a curve which he had invented and to which he gave the name ἡ ἱπποπεδη (*hippopede*, horse-fetter). The curve somewhat resembles our symbol for infinity (∞), and has been explained by the Italian astronomer Schiaparelli (1875) as the intersection of a sphere and a cylinder, and called by him a spherical lemniscate. The spirics of Perseus, mentioned above, also include a curve known as the "hippopede."

Diocles (*c*. 180 B.C.), one of the later Greek geometers, invented a curve known as the cissoid (ivy-shaped), and this was used for the purpose of duplicating the cube.

It therefore appears that the Greeks were well acquainted with certain higher plane curves and with a few curves of double curvature — although, owing to the manifold nature of these curves, it was not possible for them to exhaust the theory of this subject, great as their progress was in the theories of elementary plane geometry and of conic sections.

6. ALGEBRA

Nature of Algebra. As already stated, the Greeks of the classical period had no algebra of the kind with which we are familiar at the present time. It should be remembered, however, that our present symbolism, our methods of treating the equation, and our extensive use of mechanical manipulation are not essential to an efficient algebra, any more than our numerical symbols and our methods of calculation are essential to an efficient arithmetic. It is well, therefore, that we briefly consider the nature of algebra before we attempt to decide upon our indebtedness to the Greeks with respect to this science.

Nesselmann, in his *Die Algebra der Griechen* (Berlin, 1842), divides algebra into three general types, representing, in a general way, three periods in its history. His three types are : (1) the rhetorical, in which the words and sentences are written out in full; (2) the syncopated, in which the work is condensed by the use of abbreviations; (3) the symbolic, in which symbols, somewhat like those now in use, are introduced for the purpose of still further abbreviation. In a rough way this serves to block out the periods through which algebra has passed. The first is, generally speaking, pre-Grecian, but extends through the classical period as well; the second is late Greek and medieval; the third is modern.

This does not serve to tell us, however, what we mean by algebra, — a term which is so loosely used as to make precise definition difficult. Etymology is of little more help than it is in the case of geometry. If we examine a typical textbook on the subject, however, we find a few features which serve to give at least a general idea of the meaning of the word.

In the first place we find a modern symbolism, but this is manifestly not a necessity, although it is a convenience of a transitory type. In the second place we find a large amount of manipulation of these symbols;

but this, also, is purely modern, and hardly appears to any extent before the seventeenth century. The next feature is the equation, and this is found, usually in rhetorical form, in the Ahmes papyrus (*c.* 1550 B.C.). The fourth general topic is irrational numbers such as are needed in the solution of equations like $x^2 = 2$ and $x^3 = 5$. There will also be found what seems at first to be a minor topic, namely, the subject of proportion; but when we consider that a proportion is simply an expression of the equality between two ratios, or, as we would now say, between two fractions, we see that it is an early method of stating and solving algebraic equations. And finally, we shall find a little work in series.

Algebra has not always included these topics. The name is Arabic and was first used, so far as we know, by Mohammed ibn Musa, al-Khowârizmî, a Bagdad scholar who lived (*c.* 820) at the time referred to in *The Arabian Nights Tales.* He wrote a work entitled *al-jabr w' al muqâbalah* ("restoration and equation"), a title which appeared in the abbreviated form of "algebra" in the Latin translations. The term had,

[67]

therefore, to do with equations. Since one of the most common methods of writing a general equation, until modern times, was by means of a proportion, and since the idea of irrational numbers was expressed through ratios (as the ratio of the diagonal to the side of a square), we may say that two of the essential concepts of algebra are proportion and ratio, the latter including the idea of the irrational.

Pre-Grecian Algebra. Long before the Greeks gave any attention to mathematics the Egyptians had solved number puzzles which would now be considered as algebraic. They had a hieroglyphic combination which is usually transliterated as *ahe, ha'*, or *hau*, which meant "mass" or "heap," and this term was used to represent the unknown quantity. They could write an equation in the rhetorical form, and on rare occasions they used symbols for addition, subtraction, and equality. Such an equation is given in the Ahmes papyrus as "Mass, its whole, its seventh, it makes 19." The Egyptians were also able to solve such a problem as that of finding two numbers the sum of whose squares is 100, one number being three-fourths the other. They solved all their equations by trial and error, — a kind of systematic guessing at results and correcting the mistakes.

The Chinese may also have been equally far advanced in a primitive type of algebra before the Greeks developed their mathematics, but we are too uncertain regarding their early literature to be positive as to the dates and authenticity of their classics.

Algebra in Greece. With this rapid sketch of the general meaning of algebra and of the state of the science before the Greek ascendancy, we are now prepared to consider the significance of two passages found in the scholarly work by Dr. Allman, *Greek Geometry from Thales to Euclid,* based upon an opinion previously advanced by Comte.

"Thales may . . . be fairly considered to have laid the foundation of Algebra, for his first theorem establishes an equation in the true sense of the word, while the second institutes a proportion."

The theorems to which he refers, and which are conjecturally ascribed to Thales, are as follows :

[69]

(1) "The sum of the three angles of a triangle is equal to two right angles;

(2) "The sides of equiangular triangles are proportional."

The second passage from Dr. Allman's work is as follows: [12]

"One chief characteristic of the mathematical work of Pythagoras was the combination of arithmetic with geometry. The notions of an equation and a proportion — which are common to both, and contain the first germ of algebra — were, as we have seen, introduced amongst the Greeks by Thales. These notions, especially the latter, were elaborated by Pythagoras and his school, so that they reached the rank of a true scientific method in their Theory of Proportion. To Pythagoras, then, is due the honour of having supplied a method which is common to all branches of mathematics, and in this respect he is fully comparable to Descartes, to whom we owe the decisive combination of algebra with geometry."

It is not likely that students of mathematics will agree with respect to the first point which Dr. Allman endeavors to make, — that the fact that Thales may

possibly have known a special geometric
equality is proof that the general notion
of an algebraic equation is due to him.
When, however, Dr. Allman speaks of
Thales as having used a proportion, the assertion is perfectly true that here is an important advance in the field of algebra, even
though the problem to which it applied is
geometric.

The ancient *arithmetica* was, as we have
seen, the theory of numbers. These numbers the Greeks commonly represented by
lines and rectangles, as in the works of
Euclid and of Theon of Smyrna. At present we treat of the problems relating to this
theory by algebraic methods, although the
Greeks used geometric figures to assist them;
but their whole treatment of ratio, proportion, and the number theory may properly
be taken to be a phase of algebra.

For example, Hippocrates, in the fifth
century B.C., was interested in the dupli-
cation of the cube. He discovered that the
problem can be solved by finding two mean
proportionals between two lines, one line
being double the other. With our present
symbols we can easily see that, if we have

$$a : x = x : y = y : 2\,a,$$

then $\qquad x^2 = ay, \quad y^2 = 2\,ax, \quad x^4 = a^2y^2,$

and $\qquad\qquad x^4 = 2\,a^3x,$

and hence $\qquad x^3 = 2\,a^3.$

In other words, we see that the cube of which the edge is x is twice the cube of which the edge is a. We represent by algebraic symbols what Hippocrates represented by lines and treated by proportion. Moreover, the Greeks could solve these equations by the aid of geometric curves, whereas no predecessor of Thales had any means for accomplishing this result.

In general, therefore, the Greeks of the pre-Alexandrian Period were able to treat of surd numbers by the aid of ratios of lines, and to solve some rather difficult equations by means of proportion and by the aid of geometry.

Euclid, in his *Data* (Δεδομένα, *dedomena*), gives a number of propositions which involve essentially the equations of a straight line and a hyperbola. For example:

"If two straight lines contain a parallelogram given in magnitude in a given angle, and if the sum of the straight lines be given, then shall each of them be given."

[72]

This is a general case involving the special set of equations, $xy = k^2$ and $x + y = a$, and from it x and y can be found; or, as Euclid has it, "then shall each of them be given." He also considered the following cases:

$$xy = k^2, \quad x - y = a \quad \text{(Problem 84)},$$
$$xy = k^2, \quad x^2 - y^2 = a^2 \quad \text{(Problem 86)}.$$

In his *Elements* (II, 11) Euclid solved essentially the following equations:

$$x^2 + ax = a^2$$
$$x^2 + ax = b^2,$$

the basis of his method being related to that of completing the geometric square, although the method itself, due to the Pythagoreans, is known as the "application of areas." In its most general form it has no longer any significance in algebra. Negative roots were neglected in all cases.

Algebraic Methods. The geometric method, employed until after Euclid's time, gradually gave way to a rather crude algebraic method, and about the beginning of the Christian era Heron was able to solve the equation $144 x (14 - x) = 6720$, which required larger numbers than had been generally used in quadratics of this nature. There is also

[73]

an equation that is doubtfully assigned to him, namely,

$$\tfrac{11}{14} x^2 + \tfrac{29}{7} x = 212,$$

which may have been solved by pure algebraic methods.

With Diophantus (*c.* 275), the algebraic method definitely replaced the geometric. In his works there appeared a symbolism worthy the name and quite as usable as any other that is found before the sixteenth century. It is because of this fact and his skill in solving quadratic equations, and because of the further fact that his *Arithmetica* was the first treatise devoted wholly to algebra, that Diophantus is often looked upon as the Father of the science.

The transition from the geometric to the algebraic method may be seen in the fact that Euclid and Apollonius would have refused to add an area to a line, that is, to consider a case like $x^2 + x$. Heron, however, gives a problem substantially as follows:

"If *S* is the sum of the area *A*, the circumference *C*, and the diameter *d* of a circle, find the value of *d*."

[74]

Mr. Gow, in his *Short History of Greek Mathematics*, gives a conjectural solution, as follows:

$$A = \tfrac{1}{4}\,\pi d^2 \text{ and } C = \pi d.$$

Then $S = \tfrac{1}{4}\,\pi d^2 + (\pi + 1)d = \tfrac{11}{14}\,d^2 + \tfrac{29}{7}\,d$, π being taken as $\tfrac{22}{7}$.

Multiplying by 11×14,

$$121\,d^2 + 638\,d + 841 = 154\,S + 841,$$

whence $\quad (11\,d + 29)^2 = 154\,S + 841.$

Heron gives the answer

$$d = \tfrac{1}{11}\,(\sqrt{154\,S + 841} - 29),$$

which is the one that follows from the above equation. It therefore appears that Heron must have had some kind of algebraic rule or method for solving quadratic equations of a considerable degree of difficulty.

Diophantus uses only a single unknown quantity, which he calls "the number" (ὁ ἀριθμός, *ho arithmos*), representing it by a symbol which seems to have been formed from the syllable αρ (*ar*). He calls the square of the unknown "the power," also representing it by a combination of the first two letters of the word δύναμις (*dynamis*, whence "dynamo" and "dynamic"). The cube of the unknown he called "the cube," representing it by a combination of the first two letters of κύβος (*kubos*). The next three powers were called δυναμοδύναμις (*dynamodynamis*), δυναμόκυβος (*dynamokubos*), and κυβόκυβος (*kubokubos*), — which was as far as he went.

Indeterminate Equations. The indeterminate equation, at least in the form of a number puzzle, was probably in evidence before the Greek period. To find the positive integers whose sum is 12, or those whose product is 32, would, for example, naturally be an interesting puzzle for children, as we find to be the case in the elementary school today.

It is, however, in the quadratic cases that problems of any difficulty arise, and the study of these cases begins with the Pythagoreans. Proclus tells us that Pythagoras himself gave a rule for finding certain classes of roots of the equation $x^2 + y^2 = z^2$, — an equation connected with the so-called Theorem of Pythagoras. This rule, as handed down by tradition, may be expressed in modern symbols as follows:

$$n^2 + \left(\frac{n^2 - 1}{2}\right)^2 = \left(\frac{n^2 + 1}{2}\right)^2,$$

where n is an odd number.

Plato gave a rule which we may express as $(2n)^2 + (n^2 - 1)^2 = (n^2 + 1)^2$, and Sir Thomas Heath has shown that this, like the one attributed to Pythagoras, is connected with Euclid's assertion relating to so-called quarter squares, namely, that

$$\left(\frac{a+b}{2}\right)^2 - \left(\frac{a-b}{2}\right)^2 = ab.$$

Of all the Greek writers, however, Diophantus is the one who did most with indeterminate equations of the second degree. He was searching in general for classes of numbers instead of particular numbers, and it is the class, as such, that is primarily sought in an indeterminate equation. For example, one of his problems may be stated as follows: [13]

"To add the same [required] number to two given numbers so as to make each of them a square."

If the two given numbers are, say, 2 and 3, then $x + 2$ and $x + 3$ must both be squares, and he finds the value of x in this case to be $\frac{97}{64}$.

The following problem represents one of the more difficult types:

"To find three numbers such that their sum is a square and the sum of any pair is also a square."

The results given by Diophantus for this problem are 80, 320, and 41.

The most famous of all the indeterminate problems that have come down to us is the so-called Cattle Problem, doubtfully attributed to Archimedes. Stated in modern form, the problem is to find the number of bulls of four colors,—white (W), blue (B), yellow (Y), and piebald (P), — and also the number of cows of the same colors $(w, b, y,$ and $p)$, such that

$$B = (\tfrac{1}{4} + \tfrac{1}{5})\,(Y + P)$$
$$P = (\tfrac{1}{6} + \tfrac{1}{7})\,(W + Y)$$
$$w = (\tfrac{1}{3} + \tfrac{1}{4})\,(B + b)$$
$$b = (\tfrac{1}{4} + \tfrac{1}{5})\,(P + p)$$
$$p = (\tfrac{1}{5} + \tfrac{1}{6})\,(Y + y)$$
$$y = (\tfrac{1}{6} + \tfrac{1}{7})\,(W + w)$$

Reduced to a single equation the problem involves the solution of the indeterminate quadratic

$$x^2 - 4{,}729{,}494\,y^2 = 1,$$

and the number of bulls, for example, has 68,848 periods of three figures each.

Cubic Equations. The Greeks did not limit their interest in algebra to linear and quadratic equations, for on three noteworthy occasions they made an attempt to solve the cubic. We have seen, for example, that Hippocrates of Chios (*c.* 460 B.C.) attempted to find two mean proportionals between a and $2\,a$, which problem requires substantially the solution of the incomplete cubic equation $y^3 = 2\,a^3$.

Archimedes also investigated the problem of cutting a sphere by a plane so that the two segments shall have a given ratio. The problem reduces to the solution of the proportion

$$c - x : b = a^2 : x^2,$$

which is essentially the equation

$$x^3 + a^2 b = c x^2.$$

Eutocius (*c.* 520) tells us that Archimedes solved it by finding the intersection of the parabola $x^2 = \dfrac{a^2}{c}\, y$ and the hyperbola $y(c - x) = bc$.

The third noteworthy cubic solved by the Greeks arose in connection with the following problem, which was stated by Diophantus: [14]

"To find a right-angled triangle such that the area added to the hypotenuse gives a square, while the perimeter is a cube."

The problem involves the cubic equation

$$x^3 + x = 4x^2 + 4.$$

We do not know how Diophantus solved it, because he simply says that x " is found to be" 4. It is possible that he reduced the equation to the form

$$x(x^2 + 1) = 4(x^2 + 1)$$

and saw that this equation is satisfied if $x = 4$.

Elementary Series. The sequence of numbers in an arithmetic or geometric progression was recognized by both the Egyptians and the Babylonians, as is seen in the papyri and the cylinders. Ahmes, for example, gives problems involving each of these kinds of series and gives solutions which show that he had a rule for finding sums and such other elements as the nth term and the difference. Such knowledge was part of the Greek inheritance from the older civilizations.

What, then, were the contributions of Greece? Briefly stated, they were of three kinds: (1) they greatly simplified the treatment of the series already known; (2) they introduced the study of higher types; (3) they made the first steps toward the investigation of infinite series.

With respect to arithmetic progressions the Pythagoreans connected the theory with figurate numbers, recognizing, for example, that the triangular number

$$1 + 2 + 3 + 4 + \ldots + n$$

is a simple case of such a series. When Diophantus (*c.* 275) wrote his *Arithmetica*, the theory was so well advanced that he was able to include such propositions as the following: (in modern symbols) if an arithmetic progression be represented by $a, a + d, a + 2d, \ldots$, the difference between the first and the nth terms is $(n - 1)d$.

With respect to geometric progressions Euclid gave a rule which amounts, in our symbols, to the following:

$$\frac{ar^n - a}{S_n} = \frac{ar - a}{a},$$

which readily reduces to our present formula for S_n.

It is doubtful which of the various discoveries attributed to Pythagoras gave him
(if, indeed, they are due to him at all) the
greatest pleasure. If mathematicians were
called upon to venture an opinion, it would
probably be that his chief contribution was
to the theory of incommensurable numbers.
It is not unlikely, however, that his chief
pleasure came from his discovery of the
dependence of the musical intervals upon
the ratios of numbers. He is said to have
shown that, with strings of equal tension,
the difference in length in the ratio of 2 : 1
gives the octave; in the ratio of 3 : 2, the
fifth; and in the ratio of 4 : 3, the fourth.
He thus connected music with number.

He also gave to his followers the relation

$$1 : \tfrac{1}{2} = (1 - \tfrac{2}{3}) : (\tfrac{2}{3} - \tfrac{1}{2})$$

to which, so Iamblichus (c. 320) tells us,
Archytas and Hippasus gave the name
"harmonic proportion." It was from this
that the theory of harmonic progression
was later developed.

Infinite Series. The Greeks were the
first to make any advance in the subject
of infinite series. When the Eleatic school,

[82]

founded in the fifth century B.C., denied the infinite divisibility of time and space, Zeno suggested such problems as the well-known one of Achilles and the tortoise. Suppose, for example, that Achilles can run ten times as fast as a tortoise, and that the tortoise has 1000 feet the start in a race; then when Achilles reaches the point whence the tortoise started, the latter will be 100 feet ahead; when Achilles reaches that point, the tortoise will be 10 feet ahead; when Achilles arrives there, the tortoise will be 1 foot ahead, and so on, the tortoise always being one-tenth as far ahead as the distance last covered by Achilles; and so the latter can never overtake the former. Evidently we have, in this case, an infinitely decreasing geometric series, — the first one mentioned in history.

Archimedes applied such a series, — together with the method of exhaustion, which is explained later, — to the finding of the area of a parabola. The particular series which he summed was

$$1 + \tfrac{1}{4} + (\tfrac{1}{4})^2 + (\tfrac{1}{4})^3 + \cdots + (\tfrac{1}{4})^n + \cdots,$$

the result being $\tfrac{4}{3}$.

Higher Series. In the field of higher series, the Greeks were the first to make any progress. Archimedes used geometry to prove that

$$3\,[a^2 + (2\,a)^2 + (3\,a)^2 + \cdots + (na)^2] =$$
$$(n + 1)(na)^2 + a\,(a + 2\,a + 3\,a + \cdots + na),$$

which, for $a = 1$, reduces to

$$1^2 + 2^2 + 3^2 + \cdots + n^2 = \tfrac{1}{6}n(n + 1)(2\,n + 1),$$

a form which, stated as a rule, appears in the *Codex Arcerianus* (*c.* 500).

Combinatory Theory. Plutarch tells us that Xenocrates (*c.* 350 B.C.) computed the number of possible syllables capable of being made by Greek letters. He also states that Chrysippus (*c.* 250 B.C.) found the number of combinations of the ten axioms, and that Hipparchus (*c.* 140 B.C.) also considered the same problem. These cases go to show that the Greeks had some idea of the nature of combinations, although we have no evidence that they ever developed any laws relating to the theory.

7. TRIGONOMETRY

General Nature. In speaking of the rise of trigonometry it must be understood that the subject which now bears the name was developed in order to meet two entirely different needs, and that it had two radically different branches in ancient times. If we take the etymological meaning of the term (τρίγωνον + μετρεῖν, *trigonon* + *metrein*, to measure a triangle), the science goes back to the second and probably the third millennium B.C. It is found in the Ahmes papyrus in connection with five problems relating to the mensuration of pyramids, and in four of these problems mention is made of the *seqt*, or *seqet*, a word apparently meaning "ratio number." Just what ratio is intended is uncertain, but it is thought that the word refers either to the cosine or to the tangent of a certain angle connected with the pyramid.

Although in the early literature of China we find references to shadow reckoning, an illustration of the use of this method first appears in the story related concerning the measurement by Thales of the height of an Egyptian pyramid by means of shadows. From the several versions of this story it seems that Thales took the ratio of the height of a vertical staff to the length of its shadow as equal to the similar ratio with respect to the pyramid. This involves the direct shadow (the *umbra recta* of the Middle Ages), which eventually led, with the gnomon, to the idea of the tangent of an angle. This function is naturally the one to be first considered, and, since it is connected with the shadow of the gnomon on a sundial, it could hardly have failed to interest astronomers.

Aristarchus of Samos (*c.* 260 B.C.), or possibly Eudoxus (*c.* 370 B.C.), made the most notable advance in the applications of this primitive trigonometry. He attempted to find the distances from the earth to the sun and the moon, and also the diameters of these bodies. In this attempt he made use of correct geometric methods, introducing a ratio which is substantially the tangent of an angle, but his instruments were lacking in the degree of precision necessary to secure satisfactory results. In his work he also assumed the equivalent of the proposition which asserts that, if A and B are two acute angles, A being greater than B, then

$$\frac{\tan A}{\tan B} > \frac{A}{B} > \frac{\sin A}{\sin B},$$

but he had no knowledge of these functions as such.

It thus appears that the Greeks contributed to a noteworthy extent to the development of plane trigonometry, recognizing substantially one of our functions, and possibly two.

The most important step taken with respect to trigonometry in ancient times, however, was in connection with the study of the sphere. This accounts for the fact that spherical trigonometry kept pace for some time with the study of plane triangles, and finally passed it.

Contributions to Spherical Trigonometry. The oldest of the extant Greek works on spherics are those of Autolycus of Pitane (*c.* 350 B.C.), but although they treat of the principal circles of the sphere, they do not touch upon the question of trigonometry.

The first of the great mathematical astronomers of antiquity was Aristarchus of Samos, who has already been mentioned. He is credited by various ancient writers as being the originator of the heliocentric hypothesis, — a theory which was thus set forth nearly two thousand years before

Copernicus, and by one whom the latter acknowledged as its author.

The greatest of the mathematical astronomers of Greece was Hipparchus (*c.* 140 B.C.). His writings lead us to believe that he gave much attention to the graphic solution of spherical triangles. In this work he used the chord of an arc, that is, twice the sine of half the central angle. It is also thought that, in order to compute the table of chords which he is reported to have left, he must have known the equivalent of our formulas for $\sin (A \pm B)$ and $\cos (A \pm B)$. These formulas are also involved, although not expressly stated, in certain propositions in Euclid's *Elements* (Book VI). It is because of his work on the table of chords, — the first table of trigonometric functions extant, — that Hipparchus is often known as the Father of Trigonometry.

Heron of Alexandria (*c.* 50, or possibly as late as 200) wrote extensively on mensuration. In his treatment of regular polygons he gave certain rules which are sometimes considered as involving the idea of plane trigonometry, but he contributed nothing of importance to the subject. A generation or so later, Menelaus (*c.* 100) made a careful study of spherical triangles and wrote six books on chords of arcs and a work on spherics. He set forth an important theorem involving the chords of six arcs, this being known in the Middle Ages as the *Regula sex quantitatum.* The rule may be due to Hipparchus, or possibly to Euclid, but at any rate it is Greek in its origin.

Ptolemy the astronomer (*c.* 150) computed a new table of chords and made at least one advance upon the works of his predecessors; he used the half chord in certain cases, this being the equivalent of the sine of the half angle. He also knew the equivalent of our Law of Sines, namely,

$$\frac{a}{\sin A} = \frac{b}{\sin B} = \frac{c}{\sin C},$$

although he expressed it by means of chords. He used the right-angled spherical triangle, and knew essentially the following formulas:

$$\cos c = \cos a \cdot \cos b,$$
$$\cos A = \tan b \cdot \cot c,$$
$$\sin b = \tan a \cdot \cot A.$$

These formulas were in rhetorical form, since these functions were not yet invented.

[89]

III. INFLUENCE OF THE CON-
TRIBUTIONS

1. LOGISTIC

Notation. What do we owe to the classical notation, and what has been the influence of that notation upon the arithmetic of the fifteen centuries that have elapsed since the Fall of Rome?

In the first place we owe to the ancients our technical vocabulary, not merely that of mathematics in general and of notation in particular, but that of all the sciences. The North was able to contribute the language of the chase, the field, and the home, but it took a much more mature civilization to contribute the language of science, the camp, the fine arts, religion, and philosophy. This contribution may therefore be accepted as a natural condition, and only a few of the more interesting instances will be mentioned.

Why, for example, should we speak of notation in connection with the writing of numbers? Since the word *nota* (from *noscere*, to know) was used to denote a mark designed to call attention to something known, it was employed, even in classical times, to mean a shorthand symbol of any kind. Hence Boëthius speaks of the shorthand symbols of music as *notae* (our musical "notes") and in a doubtful passage in his geometry the shorthand symbols for one, two, three, and the like were also called by the same name. Since the latter symbols were used more often than the former by medieval writers, the word "notation" came to be employed more frequently in connection with numbers than as related to musical notes, although the latter usage was not uncommon in the Middle Ages and has remained until the present day.

The most common of the several Greek notations was characterized by such symbols as Π, Δ, Η, and Χ and was no better than the Roman notation, with its corresponding symbols V, X, C, ∞ (CIƆ, or M). The Roman system was, as we have seen, substantially identical with the Greek, except as to the characters themselves, particularly those representing very large numbers, and so the influence of the one was much the same as that of the other. For reasons set forth in Chapter II, the Roman numerals satisfied all the purposes of bookkeeping in the Middle Ages, and hence they remained in use until comparatively recent times. Since they were more easily incised than those employing a larger number of curved lines, and since they harmonize more with the architectural features of a stone building, they are still extensively used for monumental inscriptions of various kinds. Although from time to time they changed more or less in form, especially in the late Middle Ages and in the Renaissance, and although a symbol like MCM would not have been used in classical times, the general plan at present employed in writing numbers on this system is quite like the one in use at the beginning of the Christian era.

The Common Operations. The common operations are so closely connected with the modern numerals that the classical influence is noticeable only in the terminology. It should be recalled that we have no works on logistic that date from the classical period, but the later Latin writers give us what were probably the early terms in common use. These writers spoke of the *numeri addendi* (numbers to be added), from which the sixteenth-century arithmeticians coined the word "addends" (*addendi*). To the result in addition they gave such names as *summa*, *productus*, and *numerus collectus*. Hence we might, with historical accuracy, speak of the result in addition as the "product" or the "collect." Perhaps the Church use of the latter convenient and suggestive term interfered with its being employed in addition; the rise of the rule in all kinds of instruction, with the resulting demand for brevity of expression, seemed to require a special name for the result in multiplication, and so the word "product" became limited to that operation.

We speak of the taking of one number from another as subtraction (*sub*, under, + *trahere*, to draw), a word bequeathed to the schools by the late Latin writers. It would be simpler to say "I take" instead of "I subtract," and this was done by the great medieval mathematician, Leonardo Fibonacci (1202), who used such words as *tollo*, *aufero*, and *accipio*, and who also used, with much reason, the word "extract" (*extrahere*, *ex-*

tractum). The Italian algebraist, Cardan
(1545), used the suggestive form "detract"
(*detrahere, detractum*). Of all the Latin
forms, however, the one which has survived
most vigorously, outside the schoolroom, is
"deduct" (*deducere, deductum*), and this is
the one commonly used in business today. A
curious modification of the Latin word
subtractio began to appear in the late Middle
Ages, finding its way into the arithmetics
printed in Paris about 1500. Perhaps due
to the French *sous*, as in *soustraction*, and
perhaps for the sake of analogy (cf. the word
"abstract" instead of "abtract"), *subtractio* was modified to *substractio*, and for
two or three centuries it remained the standard form in Europe, also appearing (as "sub-
straction") in the first native American
arithmetic (1729) printed in the English
colonies. It survives even today, confined
chiefly to those of rather inferior education.

The words "minuend" and "subtrahend,"
now generally meaningless to children when
they learn them, are from the Latin *numerus
minuendus* and *numerus subtrahendus*, expressions that conveyed definite meanings

in the days when Latin was understood by those who studied or taught arithmetic.

It is not unusual in algebra to hear the expression "$a + b$ into $a - b$," meaning that the product of those two binomials is to be taken; but no pupil and few teachers have any idea how "into" came to have the force of "times." The explanation reaches back to the days when the Greeks used the word πολυπλασιάζειν (*polyplasiazein*, Euclid, Diophantus, and Pappus), or πολλαπλασιάζειν (*pollaplasiazein*, Heron and also Pappus), which the Latins translated as *multiplicare*, from *multus* (many) and *plicare* (to fold). The word "multiply" therefore was the same as the North European expressions "manifold" and "many fold" (compare "three-ply" and "four-ply"), appearing in the German arithmetics of the fifteenth and sixteenth centuries in such forms as *mannigfaltigen* and *vervielfachen*. Since one thing was folded on (Latin, *in*) another, the Latin writers of the Middle Ages and the Renaissance spoke of "leading" a number "into" this manifoldedness, as when Jordanus Nemorarius (*c.* 1225) says : *Si aliquis numerus . . . ducatur;* and when Clichtoveus (1503) says: *Multiplicare, est ex ductu unius numeri in alterum numerum producere, qui toties habeat in se multiplicatum, quoties multiplicās unitatem.* Such expressions were general in the early printed books, and this explains the algebraic use of the "in" or "into," although its use in arithmetic has long since been abandoned.

As already stated, the word "product," generally limited at present to the result in multiplication, was long used instead of "sum" in addition. Indeed, etymologically and historically it may be used for the result of any operation or solution. So far as multiplication is concerned, if we have two factors ("makers"), the result should be the *factum* (thing "made"); and this term was not infrequently used by the Renaissance writers.

The terminology of division also owes much to the classical forms. The late Latin writers thought of the operation under two forms, namely, measuring and parting. For example, to divide 10 feet by 2 feet is to measure the former by the latter, thus finding how often (*quoties*) it contains it. On the other hand, to divide 10 feet by 2 is to separate 10 feet into two equal parts. Since the labeling of numbers by such words as "feet" and "pounds" is a relatively late notion of the schools, the earlier writers commonly took, for indicating division, one name or the other according to preference, although some used the two interchangeably. Thus Euclid (*c.* 300 B.C.) used the expression "to measure" (μετρεῖν, *metrein*), while Heron, Pappus, and Diophantus, living a few centuries later, preferred the phrase "to part" (μερίζειν, *merizein*). This double usage accounts for such expressions among the English arithmeticians of the sixteenth century as "Deuision or partition" (Baker, 1568) and "To deuide or parte" (Digges, 1572).

Powers and Roots. The teacher of involution and evolution who does not know something of our indebtedness to the classical ideas will find himself confined to a more or less mechanical treatment of the subject. If "multiply" signifies folding one surface upon another, we may readily see how, if a number is repeatedly folded upon itself, it is, as it were, rolled up (in-volved) or turned upon itself; whereas, if the result is then unrolled (e-volved), we come back eventually to the number with which we started.

It would be interesting, moreover, to inquire of a body of teachers why they speak of "powers" and "roots" of numbers, what a "radical" in algebra has to do with a radical in politics or with a radish from the garden, why we "extract" a root although we merely "find" a quotient, and why an English teacher will speak of "root 2" when an American says "the square root of 2."

The Arab writers, beginning in the ninth century, obtained their mathematics from two sources, the Greek and the Hindu, doubtless also with some influence from Chinese writers. They translated the leading mathematical works of Greece, but they modified the knowledge thus secured by combining with it the convenient number system which, we infer, came to them from India. The Greek mathematics was based chiefly upon geometry; the Hindu, upon number. When the Greek writers of the classical period thought of a number multiplied by itself, they visualized a square array, and so they spoke of the number as a square number. If the

[98]

square number was given, they thought of each factor as the side of that square. This idea was passed over to the Romans, who spoke of the *latus* (side) of a *quadratus*, or *numerus quadratus*. If a square was given, the Latin arithmetician "found" the *latus*.

The Arabs, however, having a more convenient numeral system, were less confined to geometric forms in arithmetic. Apparently following the Hindu lead, they thought of a power as springing, like a plant, from its root. When the *libri algorismi*, already mentioned, were translated from the Arabic into the Latin, beginning about the twelfth century, they brought the word *radix* (root) into Europe as a synonym of the original Latin term *latus*. Since, however, we pull out a root from the ground, they translated this expression as *ex-trahere* (*extractum*), and so we obtained our modern and rather meaningless term. Hence the Roman "found the side" and the Arab "extracted the root," and the power of algorism brought the latter term into common use in the schools. The Latin arithmetics, however, preferred the use of *latus* until the end of the sixteenth century.

[99]

Since *radix* thus came into use, the adjective "radical" became necessary, and this came finally to be looked upon as a noun, as when we speak of studying radicals. The connection of the term with the word "radish," and with one who thinks he goes to the "root" of things and thus likes to call himself a radical, is apparent.

When Diophantus (*c.* 275) wrote his great treatise on the theory of numbers (ἀριθμητική, *arithmetike*), he evidently conceived of 3 × 3 as more powerful than three alone, and so he spoke of it as the "power" of three. He did not speak of the "second power," because δύναμις (*dynamis,* power) was taken to mean "second power." If he, like his Greek forbears, had visualized the concept geometrically, he would have spoken of the "square" of three. When they reversed the operation, the classical writers spoke of the side (*latus*), and it was not necessary to say that it was the side of a square. Hence when *radix* replaced *latus*, for the reasons above given, the custom was sufficiently established to allow "root" to stand for "square root." When, in the sixteenth century, the symbol √ was invented to indicate a root, the index 2 was omitted for the same reason. Thus "root three" means the square root of three in England and her dependencies, although in the United States we speak of "the square root of three," even though we quite inconsistently write $\sqrt{3}$ instead of $\sqrt[2]{3}$.

The operation of finding the square root of a number is distinctly Greek. A square was simply separated into four parts, a^2, ax, ax, and x^2, as here shown. Given the whole square, it was a simple geometric process to find a and then to find x, and to continue this as far as desired.

ax	x^2
a^2	ax

a x

Such a figure is given in Euclid's *Elements* and the arithmetical process is explained by Theon of Alexandria (*c.* 390). This process was used by the Arabs, and through them it found its way back into Europe.

2. INFLUENCE UPON METHODS OF CALCULATION

Influence of the Roman Abacus. The leading methods of calculating that were in general use from the beginning of the Christian

era to the fourteenth century in Southern
Europe and to the sixteenth century in
Northern Europe, and in China from the
twelfth century and in Japan from the sixteenth century to the present time, were derived from the Roman abacus. They were
changed in some particulars, but in their
large features they were essentially Latin.
Although there were variants of one kind and
another, the general plan was to consider
as unity a counter on the lowest line, and as
five a counter in the space above it or in a
shorter segment of the same line, and so on
up the scale. This arrangement is related
to, and perhaps based upon, the Roman use
of V, L, and D, for five, fifty, and five hundred,
respectively, and a similar set of symbols in
the Greek system. The late Roman abacus
had a long segment of the first line for the
units one, two, three, and four, and a short
segment for one five and two fives, the two
fives being the same as one on the ten-line.
We do not know how this form of the abacus
found its way to China, where it appeared
about the twelfth century, but the resemblance
is so close that we are forced to conclude that
in some way Chinese computers learned of

the device, perhaps through the intercourse of the Far East with Central Asia, where the abacus may have remained in use from Roman times. The Chinese made a larger instrument than any Roman one of which we have a record, and they arranged the beads so that they would slide on bamboo rods; but in general form the Roman device was reproduced in the Chinese *swan pan*. In the sixteenth century, as already stated, the Japanese adopted the instrument, pronounced the name *soroban*, improved upon the shape of the beads, left only one bead on the five-line, and thus obtained an instrument that is likely to remain in use until Japan, like the West, adopts some convenient and inexpensive form of the more elaborate computing machine.

The late Roman instrument, with the counters sliding in grooves, was never generally adopted in Northern Europe, but some time between the Fall of Rome and the twelfth century the line abacus with loose counters came into common use. In this form the fives, fifties, five hundreds, and so on were represented by counters in the spaces between the lines. We are ignorant of the technique of calculation employed in Europe during a period of several centuries, say from 500 to 1200 A.D., and we can only assert that, when counters reappeared, the general principle of the line abacus, although not the precise form, was the same as that of the Romans.

Since the ancients transmitted their abacus to the medieval computers, and since we know that, when the necessity arose, the latter would "borrow" a counter from a line and repay the debt by placing two counters in the space below, our modern expression "to borrow one" is a relic of the days when the borrowing involved something tangible. Similarly, when a line had five counters these were removed and a single counter was "carried" to the space above, which gave rise to our expression "to carry one."

Influence of the Greek Abacus. The Greek abacus does not seem to have recognized the five-space or five-line; at any rate, from our meager knowledge of its form, we are led to this conclusion. It would seem that the Greek computer placed as many as nine counters on a line, ten counters resulting in the taking up of this number and "carrying one " to the tens' line. Just as the Roman abacus influenced the one which was adopted in Western Europe, so the Greek form seems to have had its influence on Eastern Europe. The distinctive feature (the ten-lines instead of the five-spaces or five-lines) is found in the Armenian *choreb*, the Russian *stchoty*, and the Turkish *coulba*, all of which are of the same form. The Russians occasionally speak of their *stchoty* as a Chinese abacus, thus partially confirming the hypothesis that is sometimes expressed that it was introduced from China; but the general form is Greek, although the method of stringing the beads is Chinese. It therefore seems reasonable to suppose that this abacus represents an inherited Greek device, just as the *swan pan* is apparently a relic of the one used by the Romans.

Modern Calculating Machines. It is evident that the idea of our modern calculating machine finds its root in the Greek abacus. When Pascal (1642), seeking to save himself unnecessary labor in assisting his father make up his accounts, invented the first modern adding machine, he simply made a set of wheels which were geared in such a way that the figure 1 would be carried when ten appeared in units' place. In other words, he invented a machine that would do automatically what had been done by hand on the Greek abacus. Leibniz (1673) added to this a further device that permitted of multiplication as well as addition, and from that time to the present adaptations of the idea of the abacus have continued and improved until we now have numerous types of instruments for all the kinds of numerical calculation; all of these, however, go back to the abacus.

Finger Symbolism. In the Middle Ages and the Renaissance period there appeared several works upon numerical finger symbolism. The first to treat the subject with any care was Bede's work, *De loquela per gestum digitorum*, written about 725. That a monk secluded in a cloister in Jarrow, England, away from those great international fairs which, on the Continent, rendered this kind of numerical symbol commercially useful, — that such a student should have prepared a a book upon this subject can best be explained by the fact that the classical learning was still esteemed in these ecclesiastical centers of scholarship. It is from this work that we have most of our knowledge of the subject in the early medieval period.

Six centuries later, Nicholas Rhabdas (*c.* 1340), a Greek writer from Smyrna, wrote a treatise upon the subject (Ἔκφρασις τοῦ δακτυλικοῦ μέτρου, *Ekphrasis tou daktylikou metrou*).[15] This is less surprising in his case, in view of the fact that he lived in a part of the world where the system was in actual use. Our third leading source of information on the subject is the *Abacus atque vetustissima, veterum latinorum per digitos manusq3 numerandi*, a work written by Johannes Aventinus (Johann Thurnmayer), a Bavarian, and published at Nürnberg in 1522. Besides these standard treatises the subject is referred to in the works of such early writers as Pliny, Capella, and St. Augustine, and is treated with some care in the arithmetics of Andrés (Valencia, 1515), Recorde (London, *c.* 1542), De Moya (Salamanca, 1562), and various other well-known writers of the sixteenth and seventeenth centuries.

In general, the numbers below a hundred, being those most frequently in use, are represented in the same way by all writers,

[107]

but the higher numbers are not so well standardized. Thus the early attempts at a digital notation that should be international, apparently Greek in origin but probably used more extensively by the Romans, endured until modern times, and the system is still occasionally found in the bazaars of the Near East.

3. ARTIFICIAL NUMBERS

Common Fractions. Our common fractions, a term which relates to the common way of writing a fraction like $\frac{3}{4}$, came to us from the Arabs, who seem to have first suggested the bar between numerator and denominator. The Arabs seem to have received them, but without the bar, from the Hindus. The Hindus were apparently influenced in all their mathematics by the Greeks who settled in Northern and Central India after the Alexandrian invasion, and by the general spread of knowledge along the paths of trade. How much the Greek method of writing fractions may have influenced them we do not know, but from such knowledge as we have it would be reasonable to infer that the idea of fractions with numerators of any desired size may well have been suggested to them by those who knew of the works of Archimedes, Heron, or Diophantus.

Our name for fraction is, as already stated, Latin in origin, and the words "numerator" (numberer) and "denominator" (namer) are Latin in form. If a pupil does not know their original meanings, they are barbarisms; if he does know them, they take on new significance.

Sexagesimal Fractions. From the Greek astronomers came our division of angles into degrees, minutes, seconds, thirds, and so on, out of which we have preserved the first three, — that is, the units as far as seconds. Because the priest astronomers were the keepers of the time, the Greek ὥρα (*hora*, hour) was also divided into minutes and seconds, and so we have these relics of the ancient sexagesimal fractions in our present awkward system of angle and time measure. The relation of the Greek system to the Babylonian has already been mentioned.

Surds. Because the Pythagoreans showed that the diagonal and the side of a square have no common measure, we speak of them as "incommensurable." Because the diagonal is $\sqrt{2}$ if the side is 1, we speak of numbers like $\sqrt{2}$ as incommensurable numbers. Because they have, with respect to unity, no ratio that can be expressed by natural numbers, they are also called "irrational numbers." The Arabs took this Latin idea and spoke of these numbers as "non-expressible." It was probably this that also led them to call such numbers "inaudible," a term which returned to Europe in the medieval Latin form of *surdus* (deaf), from which we have our "surd numbers."

Logarithms. Although the ancients had no idea of logarithms, there are one or two features relating to this kind of number that are worthy of mention in this connection. The invention of logarithms was approached at about the same time, by two independent workers, proceeding from two different angles. Napier (1614) had in mind two lines, — the sine and its logarithm. He described his original invention in these words : [16]

"The Logarithme therefore of any sine is a number very neerely expressing the line, which increased equally in the meane time, whiles the line of the whole sine [that is, the radius] decreased proportionally into that sine, both motions being equal-timed, and the beginning equally swift."

Bürgi, a Swiss watchmaker, based his invention upon the principle first found in somewhat tangible form (although not definitely expressed) in the works of Archimedes, and represented in modern algebraic symbols by the identity $a^m a^n = a^{m+n}$. Napier constructed a table of logarithms of sines, although not to the convenient base 10; while Bürgi constructed a table of antilogarithms using the decimal base. Bürgi apparently was the first to complete his table, which was not printed until 1620; but Napier was the first to make his theory known in print (1614).

Each went back to the mathematics of the classical period for his fundamental principle, Bürgi the more evidently so in his dependence upon Archimedes. In neither case, however, are we justified in asserting that the concept of a logarithm is of ancient origin.

Conclusion. In general, therefore, the influence of the Greek fractions was probably

[111]

indirectly potent in the making of our common fractions; but with respect to our sexagesimal forms (as in hours, minutes, and seconds), we owe the entire system to such astronomers as Hipparchus and Ptolemy.

As to irrational numbers, we owe their development to Greece and the terminology to Rome. But far more than this, we owe to Euclid's definition of proportion the first scientific expression of the meaning of the irrational number as it occurs in such a form, and hence in an equation. This is far-reaching in its significance, for it includes essentially the meaning of the operations with irrationals. Indeed, it is not too much to say that the modern theory of the irrational merely begins where Euclid left off, and that in his work is involved the essential feature which was, in the nineteenth century, so well developed by Dedekind.[17]

4. ARITHMETIC

Theory of Numbers. In speaking of the influence of Greece upon arithmetic it must again be recalled that this term is to be taken in the ancient sense, namely, as referring to the theory of numbers and not to logistic, which is the art of calculation. This being prefaced, it is evident to anyone who considers the wide range of the number theory that it has all its roots in the Greek arithmetic, just as all our elementary geometry finds its source in the *Elements* of Euclid. Geometry has expanded greatly since the foundations were so thoroughly laid in Athens and Alexandria, and similarly with respect to the theory of numbers, but each has expanded along the lines suggested by the Greeks. The detailed tracing of the way in which new fields have opened in this theory has been thoroughly set forth by Professor L. E. Dickson, of Chicago, in his monumental treatise upon the subject, and it is therefore unnecessary, as it is also impracticable, to attempt even to summarize his results. Two lines of progress will, however, be indicated.

Consider, for example, the subject of perfect numbers, which dates back at least to Euclid, and possibly to the early Pythagoreans. There is hardly a topic in the number theory that has been and is being more critically investigated. With the study are connected the names of such medieval writers as Isidorus of Seville (*c.* 610), Alcuin of York (*c.* 775), Rabbi Abraham ben Ezra (*c.* 1140), Jordanus Nemorarius (*c.* 1225), and Leonardo Fibonacci (*c.* 1200). In the period of the Renaissance it commanded the attention of Luca Pacioli (*c.* 1485), who wrote the first general modern treatise on mathematics to appear in print (1494); Faber Stapulensis (*c.* 1500), who was one of the first French scholars to edit the arithmetic of Boëthius; Michael Stifel (*c.* 1540), one of the two leading German mathematicians of his generation; Tartaglia (*c.* 1550), one of the most prominent Italian algebraists of the sixteenth century; Robert Recorde (*c.* 1542), the founder of the school of British mathematicians; and many others of similar rank. In later times there were Descartes (*c.* 1630), the first to write on analytic geometry (1637); Fermat (*c.* 1630), the greatest genius of modern times in the theory of numbers; Mersenne (*c.* 1630), whose work in the same field was among the best; Leibniz (*c.* 1680), one of the founders of the calculus; Euler (*c.* 1760), probably the greatest mathematician that Switzerland produced; Sylvester (*c.* 1880), who may be said to have established the graduate study of mathematics in the New World; and many other mathematicians of highest rank. Hardly a better illustration could be given of the far-reaching influence of Greek thought in the field of the general theory. The number of important memoirs and chapters which have been written and published upon this seemingly elementary concept would run well up into the hundreds, and if text-books be added, that number would extend into thousands.

Similarly, when Iamblichus (*c.* 325) referred to amicable numbers as being due to the Pythagoreans, it could not have been anticipated that the theory of these numbers would attract the attention of later scholars of highest rank among the Arabs, as in the case of Tabit ibn Qorra (*c.* 870); among the Hebrews of the Middle Ages, as in the case of Ben Kalonymos (*c.* 1320); and among such writers of the modern period as Descartes, Fermat, Mersenne, and Euler.

5. ELEMENTARY GEOMETRY

General Influence of the Greeks. As already mentioned, elementary geometry in substantially all its details is Greek. The Greeks were the first people in the world, so far as we know, to attempt to prove a proposition in geometry, or even to have the concept of a strictly logical proof. They were the ones, in the school of Plato, to lay down the axioms, applicable to mathematical reasoning in general; the postulates, the bases upon which demonstrative geometry rests; and the limitations of the science, distinguishing it from what may be called higher geometry.

Euclid. The general nature of Euclid's *Elements* (*c.* 300 B.C.) has already been described. His work at once took high rank among Greek scholars and it was upon this model that Apollonius, in the third century B.C., based his treatment of conic sections. Archimedes also looked upon the *Elements* as a standard authority, referring to the propositions as if they were well known to his contemporaries.

It was natural that a book which attracted such attention should be the subject of commentaries on the part of its admirers and of adverse criticism on the part of those who can see little that is good in mathematics.

Among the latter were the Epicureans in ancient times, and those who, in this regard at least, might be dignified by the name of neo-Epicureans in these later days. Among the prominent commentators were Heron of Alexandria (*c.* 50, or possibly as late as 200), Porphyrius (*c.* 275), Pappus (*c.* 380), Proclus (*c.* 460), and Simplicius (6th century). With the exception of the works of Pappus and Proclus, most of these commentaries have been lost. To the writings of Proclus we are indebted for much of our information concerning Greek mathematics in general.

On the part of many of the smaller minds it was natural that minor points of criticism should have been advanced with respect to Euclid's sequence and his proofs; but for a successful combination of the logical and the psychological no other textbook on this subject has ever equaled it. For more than two thousand years it has been the standard to which all other writers have rallied. Its language has been simplified to meet modern needs, its logic has been softened to permit of its study by younger pupils, its propositions have been supplemented by exercises showing their applications, but the spirit of Euclid still dominates the entire teaching of geometry; and when, if ever, it ceases to do so, geometry as a science will probably disappear from our elementary schools.

The later Greeks elaborated Euclid's work to some extent, as is seen particularly in the writings of Pappus in the fourth century and of Proclus in the fifth, but the creative genius of the master was lacking and no great advance was made in elementary geometry until modern times.

The Arab civilization owed its geometry entirely to the Greeks. Euclid's works were translated into Arabic, in whole or in part, by various writers of the ninth, tenth, and eleventh centuries, and elaborate commentaries were written upon the *Elements*. The scholars of Bagdad and Cordova, however, added nothing to the Greek theory, looking upon it as approximately perfect, which, indeed, it was. Nevertheless, it is to these scholars that we owe the versions of Euclid which came to Europe in Latin translations in the twelfth and thirteenth centuries.

If Euclid had not laid down the postulate that (to use the modern version) through a given point only one straight line can be drawn parallel to a given straight line, we should not have had the non-Euclidean geometry of Bolyai and Lobachevsky in the first half of the nineteenth century. In this geometry Euclid's postulate is not accepted, and as a result another set of propositions is formed, logical in sequence and in proof but leading to conclusions that are at variance with those of Euclid, although for purposes of practical mensuration, except with very large figures, they are the same within the usual limits of accuracy.

Had there not been set forth the satisfactory sequence and method of Euclid, we should not have had the important revival of pure synthetic geometry in the nineteenth century, chiefly through the efforts of such men as von Staudt, Steiner, and Reye. Similarly, it is hardly conceivable that our projective geometry would have been thought of by Desargues (1639), Poncelet (1822), and their successors.

To the *Elements*, also, our algebra is indebted for the first systematic method of attacking the quadratic equation, namely, the method of completing geometrically the square of $x + a$ by adding to $x^2 + 2ax$ the

square of half the coefficient of x, that is, by adding a^2. Several such identities as
$$(a + b)(a - b) = a^2 - b^2$$
are first scientifically proved in Book II of the *Elements*, and thus, through the Arabic schools, they found their way from Greek geometry into the algebra of today.

And finally, with respect to our indebtedness to Euclid, our modern textbooks in mathematics are modeled primarily upon his works. Before his time these aids to teaching had been of the general type, — a mixture of various kinds of mathematics according to the taste of the writer. Illustrations of this tendency are seen in such pre-Grecian works as the Ahmes papyrus of Egypt (*c.* 1550 B.C.) and the *Nine Sections* of China, each dating, perhaps, from about the same period. Indeed, from what we know of the earlier Greek works, there was a considerable mixture of arithmetic (including what was known of algebra) and geometry. Euclid, however, made geometry the coördinating principle of mathematics and introduced into the larger science only those parts of mathematics that could profitably be treated by geometric methods. The result was a

model textbook, with the subordinate portions arranged by topics. It must also be
said for the psychological acumen of even
Ahmes and the unknown author of the
Nine Sections, that, without any coördinating principle, they had the good sense to
arrange their material topically.

It is because of the great success of Euclid's
leading work that all textbook writers who
have achieved any success have patterned,
consciously or unconsciously, upon his treatise. Demonstrative geometry has little that
naturally leads to mixing it up with modern
algebra, with trigonometry, or with physics,
and all efforts that have thus far been made
to break away from Euclid's common sense
in his topical arrangement of material have
been failures.

Terminology in Geometry. Sir Thomas
Heath has pointed out the handicap under
which a teacher labors, — not to mention
the real sufferer, the pupil, — if he has not
enough knowledge of Greek to appreciate
the etymology of the terms used in geometry.
Such a word as "isosceles," for example,
takes on new significance to the teacher who
recognizes in it the roots ἴσος (*isos*, equal)

and σκέλος (*skelos*, leg), and he can then
connect the former element with such words
as "isoperimetry" and "isothermal" and
thereby turn what is a meaningless word into
one having an aspect of familiarity.   Our
"equilateral" is a Latin term, the first part
being from the same root as "equal," and the
second from *latus* (side).   The Greeks used
ἰσόπλευρος (*isopleuros*), from ἴσος (*isos*,
equal) and πλευρά (*pleura*, side), the second
part being the root from which we have our
word "pleurisy";   the latter word comes
from πλευρῖτις (*pleuritis*, inflammation of the
side, the *itis* having the same meaning as in
appendicitis).   The pupil who learns that
"parallelogram" is a combination of παράλληλος (*parallelos*, parallel) and γραμμή
(*grammé*, line) sees in the word a new and
interesting meaning; and if he also knows
that the first of these words is itself a compound, παρ᾽ ἀλλήλας (*par' allelas*) meaning
"alongside one another"; that γραμμή
(*grammé*) comes from γράφειν (*graphein*, to
mark or write); and that γράφειν (*graphein*)
is the root of the "graphs" that he draws
in algebra, of the "phonograph" (sound-
writing), of the "telegraph" (distance-

writing), and of the "graphite" that forms the so-called lead in a pencil, then he begins to realize some of the debt that the technical language of mathematics owes to the Greeks. The fact that a parallelepiped receives its name from παράλληλος (*parallelos*, parallel) and ἐπίπεδος (*epipedos*, plane) is a matter of value as well as interest, and there is certainly pleasure in learning that "rhombus" takes its name from its resemblance to the outline of a spinning top (ῥόμβος, *rhombos*, from ῥέμβω, *rhembo*, to spin).

It will, of course, be said that it is not necessary to know much Greek to appreciate such etymologies, and this is doubtless true. On the other hand, at least some knowledge of the language is manifestly helpful to the teacher who seeks to humanize the subject of geometry, — a subject so essentially Greek as to have a large proportion of its technical terms from that source. If we do not know enough of the language to appreciate the significance of the words we use, it would be desirable to try to accomplish what seems at present impossible, viz., to bring the world to accept a simple and international vocabulary of science.

6. HIGHER GEOMETRY

Pure Geometry. Since no ancient peoples except the Greeks gave any attention to elementary demonstrative geometry, it is a mere corollary to add that none of them made any contribution to the higher branches of the science. Only among the Greeks do we find, in ancient times, a single case of a higher curve mathematically studied. Even today the conchoid of Nicomedes, the cissoid of Diocles, the quadratrix of Hippias and Deinostratus, and the spiral of Archimedes are among the curves that create the most interest on the part of students in the early stages of their work in higher geometry.

With respect to modern pure geometry, the important subject of the anharmonic ratio was considered by both Menelaus (*c.* 100) and Pappus (*c.* 380), and it may even have been known to Euclid. The proofs of the principles of poles and polars are Euclidean in nature if not in fact, as is also the case with such phases of the subject as the modern geometry of the triangle and the circle.

Analytic Geometry. Although the study of a curve by means of its equation, and *vice versa*, is an invention chiefly of the seventeenth century, several basal features of analytic geometry are found in the works of the Greeks. For example, the location of points by means of coördinates is, essentially, merely the determination of places on the earth's surface by means of latitude and longitude, — the πλάτος (*platos*) or *latitudo*, and the μῆκος (*mekos*) or *longitudo* of the Greeks and Romans, referring respectively to the width and the length of the known world lying about the Mediterranean Sea. In this manner, too, Hipparchus (*c.* 140 B.C.) located places upon the earth's surface and determined the position of stars in the celestial sphere.

The Roman *agrimensores* also fixed the points of their surveys by means of coördinates. They laid out new towns with respect to two axes, the *decimanus* (usually from east to west) and the *cardo* (at right angles to it), and their streets sacrificed the grace of curvature to the strict utility illustrated by squared paper.

In their treatment of geometric figures the Greeks recognized two axes. Archimedes, for example, used the diameter of the parabola and the tangent at the extremity of this diameter. Although Apollonius was obliged to use the rhetorical form of expression, he stated essentially the fact that the equation $x + ay = b$ represents a straight line. Sir Thomas Heath has called attention to the essential difference between the geometry of Apollonius and that of Descartes, showing that this difference lies not so much in the failure of the former to anticipate some of the ideas of the latter as in a point of view rendered necessary by the comparatively imperfect symbolism of the Greeks. He also shows that Apollonius understood the important feature of the transformation of coördinates, his conclusions being as follows : [18]

"The essential difference between the Greek and the modern method is that the Greeks did not direct their efforts to making the fixed lines of the figure as few as possible, but rather to expressing their equations between areas in as short and simple a form as possible. Accordingly they did not hesitate to use a number of auxiliary fixed lines, provided only that by that means the areas corresponding to the various terms in x^2, xy, . . . forming the Cartesian equation could be brought together and combined into a smaller number of terms. . . . In the case, then, where two auxiliary lines are used in addition to the original axes of coördinates, and it appears that the properties of the conic (in the form of equations between areas) can be equally well expressed relatively to the two auxiliary lines and to the two original axes of reference, we have clearly what amounts to a transformation of coördinates."

As to the technical terms that we use in analytic geometry, the Greeks had the equivalent of our word "ordinate," using τεταγμένως (*tetagmenos*, ordinate-wise). They spoke of "the [portion] cut off by it from the diameter towards the vertex," for which phrase we have the Latin *abscissa* (off-cut). Even our word "asymptote" was used by Apollonius, although with a somewhat different and broader meaning.

Of course, the mere relation of algebra to geometry is found all through the *arithmetica* of the Greeks, as in such identities as

$$(a - b)^2 = a^2 - 2\,ab + b^2,$$

which are so well stated in Euclid's classic.

7. ALGEBRA

Greek Influence. We tend to look upon algebra as a modern subject, or at best as an Arabic invention, but with respect to each of these ideas we are in error. The subject is modern in symbolism and Arabic in name, but the world has produced few algebraists who, for originality of method and brilliancy of action, can compare with Diophantus. He invented a symbolism, as we have already seen; it was not so convenient as ours, but it was the best that the world had known until his time. His treatment of equations was not equaled in originality or results until the sixteenth century.

Aristotle, who more than six centuries before Diophantus wrote his great work, and at a time when geometry was the sole method of approach to algebra, recognized clearly that the laws which were established by the aid of lines applied to other kinds of magnitudes, including number. In his *Posterior Analytics* he says: [19]

"Alternate proportion also, so far as regards numbers and lines and solids and times (as was once shown separately) it is possible at least to be demonstrated of all by one demonstration, but inasmuch as all these, numbers, length, time, are not one denominated thing, and differ from each other in species, they were assumed separately. But now the demonstration is universal, for it is not in so far as they are lines or numbers, that it is inherent, but in so far as this thing which they suppose to be universally inherent."

The phraseology is not what we would use, but the idea is clear, namely, that the specific demonstrations as they relate to lines are of universal validity. Aristotle had the idea; we have supplied the symbolism.

As to the Arabs, their method was Euclidean; that is, they used geometry for the purpose of developing their rules. They solved the quadratic equation, but this had been done by Euclid, Heron, and Diophantus hundreds of years before their time. They added not a single proposition of importance, nor did they make any progress toward the solution of the cubic or biquadratic equation or toward the approximation of the roots of numerical equations of higher degree. They were translators, popularizers, and textbook writers, but they were not creative algebraists.

As to the Hindus, they added nothing worthy of note to the stock of algebraic knowledge except in the way of a symbolism which no later writers adopted, and in the way of numerous interesting problems.

The Chinese, however, contributed certain ingenious devices for treating numerical higher equations, a subject which, because it was concerned with approximations rather than with precise results, had no interest for the Greeks.

8. TRIGONOMETRY

Greek Influence. Although "shadow reckoning" seems to be one of the most ancient features of mathematics, we have seen that it was the Greeks, beginning with Thales, who put it upon a scientific basis. We have also seen that they were the first to prepare a table of functions, namely, the table of chords which Hipparchus computed and which Ptolemy extended. They also suggested the half chord, that is, the sine of the half angle, and there is much evidence to support the belief that it was this suggestion

[130]

that led Āryabhata (*c.* 510), or some writer just before him, to prepare a table of these functions, apparently with the aid of the Greek tables of chords. Their work in astronomy was such as to render necessary a study of spherical trigonometry, and it is with Hipparchus that this phase of mathematical science begins.

To Babylon we are indebted for a valuable series of observations of eclipses and other celestial phenomena, but her astronomers never developed a mathematical science. The idea of the solution of a spherical triangle, for example, never seems to have occurred to any of the ancient peoples except the Greeks. Pythagoras seems to have been the first to affirm the sphericity of the earth, Eratosthenes computed the circumference as approximately 25,000 miles, Aristarchus forecast the Copernican system, and Menelaus solved the spherical triangle for four cases of a fair degree of difficulty; and these, together with the computation of tables, served to establish a science which later developed into the trigonometry which we know today, — a science improved by the Arabs, but resting upon a Greek foundation.

9. THE CALCULUS

First Steps in the Science. We commonly think of the calculus as an invention of the seventeenth century. The names which we connect with this invention are usually those of Newton and Leibniz. A contest between the followers of these two great leaders was waged for more than a century, each claiming the priority of discovery; but within the last two generations the world has come to recognize that Newton and Leibniz worked in the main independently, that they approached the subject from different standpoints, and that each is entitled to credit for the epoch-making work that he accomplished. Newton was the more original in his method and was undoubtedly the first in the field; but Leibniz developed a more convenient symbolism and was the first to publish his results. Each made a certain amount of use of the unsafe theory of infinitesimals, but Leibniz was the greater offender. Each recognized the aid received from his predecessors, but Newton was the more generous in his acknowledgment of this assistance.

It is well known that many predecessors assisted in paving the way for the invention, but the extent of our indebtedness to the Greeks is not so generally appreciated.

The calculus rests, historically, upon three mathematical concepts : (1) the infinitesimal, (2) the rate of change of one variable with respect to another, and (3) the limit.

The concept of the infinitesimal occupied the attention of various Greek philosophers. In connection with his famous paradoxes of motion, Zeno of Elea touched upon the subject, not without showing some sense of humor. Leucippus, who seems to have lived in the fifth century B.C., and who is looked upon as the founder of the atomic theory, based his philosophy upon the same concept. It is thought that he was the teacher of Democritus, who asserted that atoms are impenetrable and are separated by a vacuum. Aristotle wrote on indivisible lines and gave the first known definition of continuity. Hence the Greek philosophy had considered one of the principles upon which Cavalieri, early in the seventeenth century, based his crude form of an integral calculus, and to whom Leibniz was much indebted for his own initial steps in the theory. It should be said, however, that

[133]

neither the atomistic theory nor the idea of
the indivisible in general led the ancients
to apply their knowledge to the development of the calculus as we know it today.
They simply prepared the way, and then, so
far as relates to mathematics, abandoned the
whole matter.

As to the second concept, — the rate of
change of one variable with respect to another, — the Pythagoreans left us the powerful instrument of ratio. For the development of the theory of proportion in general
we seem to be indebted to Eudoxus (*c.* 370
B.C.), whose work may have been embodied
in Book V of Euclid's *Elements*. Thus the
idea of ratio was fully prepared to meet all
demands made upon it, and we have made no
substantial improvement upon it since Euclid's
time. While this invention was not applied
directly to rates of change, the Greeks made
much of rates of motion, as in the uniform
rates involved in constructing the quadratrix
of Hippias and Dinostratus, and in the rates
of motion in general. They had, therefore,
a basis upon which later mathematicians
could and did build in the invention of the
differential calculus.

Their influence appears clearly in the writings of Wallis and Barrow, the immediate predecessors of Newton in his work upon the fluxional calculus, as may be seen by even a cursory glance at the methods which these writers employ.

Perhaps the most important contribution of the Greeks with respect to the calculus is found in the Method of Exhaustion, since this involves the notion of a limit and is a form of integration. If, for example, we inscribe in a circle a regular polygon, say an equilateral triangle, we may easily double the number of sides and thus form a regular inscribed hexagon which has an area that is nearer than that of the triangle to the area of the circle. We may now double the number of sides again, and continue this process indefinitely, thus approaching nearer and nearer to the area of the circle. In other words, we tend to "exhaust" the difference between the area of the circle and that of the polygon. This method was used in the effort to "square the circle," that is, to find the area of the circle by constructing a rectilinear figure that was equal to it, and then constructing a square that should have the same

[135]

area as this rectilinear figure. Some of the minor Greek geometers, such as Antiphon (*c.* 430 B.C.), seem to have believed that the exhaustion was complete, but the great ones, like Eudoxus, developed the method into a rigorous theory. Archimedes used this theory in his remarkable work of squaring the parabola and in his contributions to the mensuration of the round bodies. Indeed, it is not an extravagant assertion to say that in the work of Archimedes we have as perfect a form of the integral calculus as was practicable without the aid of analytic geometry. If only Greece could have produced another Archimedes! Or if she could have held back the ravages of war and of luxury until she could have improved her symbolism and have fostered further experiment in physical lines, she would have completed the invention to which she had already so effectively contributed.

10. APPLIED MATHEMATICS

Astronomy. The subject of astronomy is treated at length elsewhere in this series, and it is neither necessary nor proper to trespass upon the territory so completely and successfully occupied by another. Mention has already been made of the great contributions of such astronomers as Hipparchus and Ptolemy to the advance of trigonometry, of such mathematicians as Menelaus to the advance of astronomy, and of such philosophers as Thales and Pythagoras to the advance of each of these sciences. It was Eratosthenes the mathematician who found the circumference of the earth to a degree of approximation not equaled by Ptolemy the astronomer, and, indeed, not equaled until modern times.

Speaking generally, it may be said that the great mathematical principles upon which astronomy rests were discovered by the Greeks. As already stated, they had a perfectly good method of measuring the earth, and they were successful in using it. The method used by them in measuring the distance to the moon was accurate from the mathematical standpoint, although it failed because of their lack of instruments of precision. In fact, the possession of telescopes of the present degree of perfection, including the vernier and the micrometer for the

reading of small angles, would have enabled
the Greeks to measure the most important
celestial distances and magnitudes with approximately our degree of precision. We
have invented many details of which they
were ignorant, we have theories in celestial
mechanics which they did not have, and we
have a number system which has given us
such tabular aids as logarithms; but the
basic principles of mathematics, used in
celestial measurements today, are found
among the many contributions which Greece
made to the advance of civilization.

Surveying and Engineering. Egypt furnished Greece with a considerable knowledge
of mensuration, including surveying and
engineering. What Greece contributed to
the subject was chiefly the demonstration
of the accuracy of the empirical rules which
had been passed on to her. She, in turn,
passed her knowledge along to Rome, and
the Roman surveyors and engineers brought
their sciences to the highest degree of perfection known to the ancient world. For
example, we have, in the work of Vitruvius
(*c.* 20 B.C.), *De Architectura Libri X*, the
contribution of one who was trained as an

engineer, who was interested in the mathematics of optics, who treated of sundials and who was evidently conversant with the mathematical principles of the architecture which Rome developed to such a high degree. We have, too, the great work of Frontinus (97 A.D.), *De Aquis Urbis Romae Libri II*, in which are set forth the details of such engineering projects as the well-known aqueducts still to be seen on the Campagna. Such undertakings show how skilled the engineers of Rome were in carrying out large undertakings. We surpass them in the fact that we have abundance of iron and steel, and we have much more carefully computed the strength of the materials needed and the pressures which they must withstand; but we have not, in general, approached them in design, nor do we seem to equal them in the durability of our structures. As to the running of levels, we do not, even with our finer instruments, seem to have improved upon their solutions of the ordinary problems which they were called upon to meet.

With respect to surveying, we have in the extant fragments of the works of Hyginus, which are included in Lachmann and Rudorff's *Gromatici Veteres*, evidence that the Roman method of laying out a field for purposes of mensuration was not essentially different from ours. Our telescope and compass were not available in Roman times, but the leveling instruments and the angle measures of the *gromatici* were quite sufficient for the ordinary work of a surveyor. What the modern world has contributed is, as in the field of astronomy, the instrument; the mathematical principles were known to the Romans. We have our modern trigonometry, but the essentially new feature here is rather our symbolism than any great basic principle.

Problems. The applied problems of mathematics change with human needs. The ancients had no need for finding the current rates of telegraphic exchange, although they were versed in the computation of drafts on such centers as Athens. They had no need for computing income tax on a sliding scale, although various forms of taxation were quite as oppressive then as now. Problems in electricity, involving perhaps a differential equation, were unknown, because they knew little of electricity and nothing of differentiation. Rome did not compute interest by the aid of our numerals, because our numerals had not yet been invented, but she computed interest in spite of this fact, and she contributed to modern life the phrase *quod est interest*, to which further reference will be made a little later; and the fact that, for a considerable period, she allowed the equivalent of $\frac{1}{2}\%$ per month has given us our common rate of six per cent *per annum*, — this phrase being purely Latin except for a single modern abbreviation.

There are certain ancient problems, however, which have found place in the textbooks of mathematics for generations, some of them for centuries, and a few of them for at least two thousand years. These problems have not endured because of the mere force of tradition; most of them have retained their place because they set forth valuable mathematical principles without involving such technicalities of trade or industry as necessitate special terms with which younger pupils are not familiar. A few of these will now be mentioned, but it should be understood that they are mere types, and that many others could be adduced as further evidence of the bonds uniting the present with the ancient civilizations.

Robert Recorde set forth a problem beginning with these words:[20]

"Ther is a cestern with iiij cocks, conteinyng 72 barrels of water, And if the greatest cocke be opened, the water will auoyde cleane in vj howers. . . ."

The problem is evidently the familiar one of the pipes filling the cistern, still found in most of our algebras, although sometimes distorted to meet supposedly modern situations. Recorde wrote the work in which this problem appears nearly four centuries ago, and so we think of the question as old. But when Recorde wrote his *Ground of Artes*, the problem had already been part of the common stock of the mathematician for at least fifteen centuries, standing forth as one of the "real" problems of the ages. It was possibly suggested by the *clepsydrae* ("water concealers"), the water clocks of the early Greek period, which very likely were introduced from Babylon. More probably it was associated with the public fountains which are still found, often in their original state, wherever the Roman civilization spread, — evidences of the technical skill of such engineers as Frontinus, and of the desire of Rome to conserve the health of her people. The problem first appears in tangible form in the Μετρήσεις (*metreseis*) which is usually attributed to Heron, and is found later in the writings of Diophantus. It forms one of the Greek epigrams, collected and apparently put in verse by Metrodorus (*c.* 500). So strongly did it appeal to the mathematical world that it found its way into the cloister schools of the Middle Ages, into the works of the Hindu scholars (as witness Bhāskara's *Lilā-vati* of *c.* 1150), into the higher class of arithmetics of the Arabs, and into many of the early printed arithmetics and algebras. With the desire of seeming to be original, many writers have changed its form, but the mathematical source is apparently Greek. We have the case of a lion, a dog, and a wolf eating a sheep at different rates of consumption, the problem being to know how long it will take if they all eat together;

we have the cases of three men building a wall, of a man and his wife drinking a cask of wine, of a ship carrying three sails of different sizes, of a mill with four sets of wheels for grinding corn, of three priests praying a soul out of Purgatory, and finally, in our day, of three pipes filling the tank of an automobile! — but in every case it is the old problem of Heron of Alexandria, which, for nearly two thousand years, has held its place as one of the most ingenious pieces of reasoning of its kind that is suited to the understanding and the interest of pupils of a certain age.

The problem of the testament of the dying man has, until within a generation or two, held place in many of the standard texts. It relates that a man made a will directing that in case an expected heir should be a boy, he should receive two thirds of the property, and that the mother should then receive one third; but that if a daughter were born, she should have one third and the mother should have two thirds. After the death of the man the mother gave birth to twins, one being a boy and the other a girl, and the question arose as to how to divide the property. The problem is purely a judicial one; the legal question being settled, the arithmetical one is simple. Such questions are common in all lands in which the right of inheritance has assumed great importance, as in parts of the Orient, in Rome, and in those parts of Europe in which the Roman law influenced the legal enactments of the various countries. In the year 40 B.C. the *Lex Falcidia* required that at least one fourth of an estate should go to the legal heir, and if this were not provided in the will the inheritance was increased to this relative amount by means of proportion, following the ordinary rules of partnership. The widow's dower right is a relic of this type of Roman legislation. The problem as stated above appears in the works of Juventius Celsus (*c.* 75), a prominent Roman authority on testamentary law, and in those of Cæcilius Africanus (*c.* 100). From that time on it was looked upon as one of the important applied problems, or at least as one which contained a principle of importance that was applicable in divers fields. It appears frequently in the manuscripts of the Middle Ages and in the early printed books of the Renaissance. It went through the usual process of modification, including the cases of triplets and cases in which the fractional parts were more complicated, and was finally abandoned because of complications in statement that were either absurd or were offensive to modern taste. For fully eighteen centuries, however, the hand of Rome was seen in this famous old testamentary puzzle.

Problems relating to interest on loans are, as already stated, of ancient origin. The Romans obtained their knowledge of the subject from the Greeks; the Greeks obtained theirs, directly or indirectly, from the Babylonians; and Europe simply followed the Roman usage. Greece seems not to have restricted the rate of interest legally, but by custom it varied from the equivalent of 12% to that of 18%, 12% being thought low, so we are told, in the time of Demosthenes. The rate was not expressed in *per cents*, but at so much per month per *mina*, or else as a certain fractional part of the principal per year, but the interest itself was usually paid at the end of each month. In Rome the interest was called *faenus* (or *fenus*) in the early days, the later term being *usura* (from *uti*, to use), ordinarily expressed in the plural, *usurae*. From this came our word "usury" and our semi-obsolete expression "with use." Since property was originally in cattle, capital was *caput* (head, originally a head of cattle), although *sors* (lot, chance) was also used. The Twelve Tables (*Duodecim Tabulae*, *c.* 450 B.C.) limited the interest charged to Roman citizens to one twelfth ($8\frac{1}{3}\%$). In later times the Romans adopted the Greek custom, apparently brought from the East, of charging by the month, 1% per month being common. Under Justinian the rate was reduced to $\frac{1}{2}\%$ per month, a rate which had already been used by the Greeks and which gave rise to our 6%. It is under the Romans that we find our percentage system. Their interest is often differentiated as *fenus unciarum* ("uncial interest," or interest reckoned by twelfths) and *usurae centesimae* ("hundredth interest"), the latter being the source of our rates *per centum* or, as we now Anglicize it, "per cent." In later times the ruling classes in Church and in State, desiring to make it difficult

[147]

for the moneyed group to amass still greater wealth, prohibited the taking of interest. They allowed, however, that, if a loan was not paid on the date when it was due, the borrower should be held to compensate the creditor by a sum which represented the difference, or "that which is between" (*id quod interest*) his respective financial positions on that day and on the day when it was actually paid. The compounding of interest was also known to the Romans and was by them transmitted to all the Latin countries.

One of the oldest of the groups of problems still found in our arithmetics relates to taxation. This application of elementary mathematics goes back to the earliest recorded history of Egypt and Babylon. The Greeks levied both direct and indirect taxes, the latter including the pentecostal (πεντη-κοστός, *pentecostos*) or "fiftieth" tax ($\frac{1}{50}$ = 2%) on imports. Rome was more efficient in her taxation (*taxare*, to evaluate), — her system including the import tax (*portarium*, from *portare*, to carry), the land tax (*tributum soli*, tribute of the land), the poll tax (*tributum capitis*, head tribute; our word "poll" comes from the northern languages, such as the Danish *bol*, a ball, bowl, bulb, or head), the tithes (*agri decumates*), and the tax on traders (*collatio lustralis*).

Our monetary problems also find connection with Rome through the fact that, as among most ancient peoples, all kinds of valuables were deposited in the temples as protection against thieves. The priests of Greece were not infrequently money lenders, and the "tables of the money changers" were found in the temples of ancient days, even as they are occasionally found in the East today. It was because of this custom that coins were first "struck" (*i.e.* with a hammer; and hence this term) in the temple of Juno Moneta (Juno the Admonisher, adviser, instructor) in Rome, whence *moneta* came to mean money, and whence we have our words "mint," "monetary," and "money." The Greek money changers, or bankers, sat by a table (τράπεζα, *trapeza*) and dealt in silver. They were therefore called ἀργυραμοιβοί (*argyramoiboi*, silver changers; Latin, *argentarii*). The late Latins translated "table" as *bancus*, whence our "bank" and "bench," and the *argen-*

[149]

tarius became a *mensularius* (from *mensa*, table). In the banking department, as distinguished from that which dealt in foreign money (the exchange department or *permutatio*), the funds of the creditor were "placed down" (*deponere, depositum*), and hence we have the modern expressions to "put you money down" and to "deposit" it.

This *depositum* was subject to a *per-scriptio* (*per + scribere*, to write, whence our physician's "prescription"), that is, a check, quite as it is at present. It drew no interest, being unproductive money (*vacua pecunia*), and this type of bank gave its name to our "bank of deposit." There developed also what we often call an "interest account," in which a *creditum* (from *credere*, to trust, whence our "creed") was placed in the bank. Since the *depositum* drew no interest it was preferred over the *creditum* in case of failure of the bank, just as our preferred stock draws its dividend (*dividendus*, that which is to be divided) before the common stock.

Of our algebraic problems, the simple number puzzle expressed by such an equation as $x + 7 = 31$ is very ancient. It is found in Egypt in the second millennium B.C., and will probably sometime be discovered among the Babylonian tablets of even an earlier time. Number puzzles of this kind come to us, however, from Greek sources. Thus Diophantus gives us the problem : "to divide a given number into two [numbers] having a given difference," illustrating it by the special case which we represent by the symbols $2x + 40 = 100$. The late Latin writers have many cases of this kind. Our indeterminate problems come in part from the same sources, and in part from the Far East.

The problems relating to the mixing of drugs, of metals for coinage and for bell founding, of alloys needed in the jewelry trade, and of tea, sugar, and the like, all go back to the solution by Archimedes of the well-known problem concerning the mixing of metals in King Hiero's crown.

11. The Teaching of Mathematics

Theories of Education. It is often asserted that one of the discouraging things about education is that such a relatively small number of intellectually strong men enter the profession. We hear the world, particularly in the newer countries, constantly lamenting this fact and referring to the days when Plato taught at Athens, Euclid at Alexandria, Alcuin at Tours, Benedict at Monte Cassino, and Arnold at Rugby. We forget that Athens, in all her brilliant career, produced but one Plato; that Alexandria, the world's first great university, produced but one Euclid; that Benedict and Alcuin stand out as two great beacon lights in a period of several centuries; and that the names of Rugby and Arnold are almost synonyms, so unique was Arnold's personality.

Nevertheless the fact remains that the educator is not infrequently lacking in a broad education and in profound scholarship in any special line, and it is therefore a matter of no surprise that many theories in his science are stillborn, or that, at best, they perish from a kind of infantile paralysis. It is part of the apparent plan of the universe that the one suggestion out of a million that is worth surviving should prove this worth through battling with the rest.

If a scholar views the various methods of teaching that are suggested for the schools, he cannot fail to be struck by the large number that seem to display considerable ingenuity in getting the pupils into habits of not learning anything well, but this fact has probably also struck other scholars in the same way in all generations. On the other hand, there are certain principles that are forcefully advanced from time to time, which seem to have such evident elements of common sense as to appeal to all thoughtful minds as likely to endure.

For example, we seek to lead children to a study of number through the use of commonplace objects, thus passing easily from the concrete to the abstract. Pestalozzi was particularly successful with this principle. Furthermore, our psychologists have become convinced that there is a high degree of correlation between quick reaction in calculation and quick reaction in other lines. Some educator comes forward every little while with the discovery that mathematics should be taught only when it "functions," which (lacking a definition of functioning) is commonly interpreted to mean

MATHEMATICS

that the subject must have an application
somewhere, and the discovery usually at-
tracts considerable local attention. Next
to this in point of popularity and frequency
comes the perennial discovery that arithmetic should be taught by games, a discovery which occasionally leads to the
theory that it should not be taught at all,
being unconsciously absorbed as the need
for it is felt.

In most of these theories there is an element of truth, but this is usually lost in the
mass of ill-considered corollaries which are
exploited along with it. But for our purposes it is interesting to note the fact that
the most hopeful of the discoveries that
are made from time to time and that have
any vitality in them are usually found in
the writings of Plato. They are not deliber-
ately pilfered from his works, for those who
advance them seem seldom to have read
the *Republic*, or the *Laws*, or the *Theætetus;*
but the ideas have so firmly impressed
themselves upon the world that they crop
up continually as bits of the general common
sense of the race.

Illustrations from Plato. Our indebted-

[154]

ness to the Greeks in the teaching of mathematics may therefore be inferred to some extent by reference to a few typical passages taken from Plato's works.

For example, our genetic psychologists search out the origin of the concept of magnitude, and are to be commended for their efforts; but wherein have they made any real advance beyond that made in the *Republic* (VII. 524)? And wherein have we, who rate highly the study of abstract number, made any clearer statement of our purpose than that which is made in the same great classic (VII. 525)? We take much interest in the recent conclusions of the psychologists that "those who have a natural talent for calculation are generally quick at every other kind of knowledge," but these are the identical words of Plato (*Republic*, VII. 526), and modern psychology is still undecided whether or not to attack his further dictum that "even the dull, if they have had an arithmetical training, although they may derive no other advantage from it, always become much quicker than they otherwise would have been."

[155]

We who are concerned with the teaching of mathematics for the soul of the subject as well as for its use in trade and in the shop, have always to meet the opposition of those who would teach only that which is immediately useful. But there is consolation, if we need it, in the knowledge that the strife is as old as the school itself, and that Plato paid his respects to this commercial type of mind in these words: [21]

"They have in view practice only, and are always speaking, in a narrow and ridiculous manner, of squaring and extending and applying and the like — they confuse the necessities of geometry with those of daily life; whereas knowledge is the real object of the whole science. . . . The knowledge at which geometry aims is knowledge of the eternal, and not of aught perishing and transient. . . . Then, my noble friend, geometry will draw the soul towards truth, and create the spirit of philosophy and raise up that which is now unhappily allowed to fall down."

Advance this statement as an argument addressed to those who see in geometry only the art of measuring as applied to the practical needs of the moment, and you are called a reactionary. But perhaps we are justified in tactfully referring to those who take the commercial position by making use of the words quoted above from the *Republic*, — that they are "always speaking in a narrow and ridiculous manner."

We find the discovery made anew, every few years, that children should be taught arithmetic by means of games, although everyone who has given the matter serious thought knows that more children, in the history of the race, have learned the elementary number relations from dice and from such games as the Italian *morra* than from textbooks. Again, it is argued that arithmetic should center about play in the school, and, indeed, that it should be a mere incident, play being the central feature. Thus we have our "number games," our "arithmetic by play," and the like, and, indeed, our most successful teachers always find that number has the same interest for children that the game has, — a satisfying of a thirst for power and knowledge. But in all this, wherein have we advanced beyond Plato? He speaks of the arith-

metic "which every child in Egypt is taught
when he learns his alphabet." And as to
the method he adds: [22]

"In that country arithmetical games have
been invented for the use of mere children,
which they learn as a pleasure and amusement.
They have to distribute apples and garlands,
using the same number sometimes for a larger
and sometimes for a lesser number of persons:
and they arrange pugilists and wrestlers as they
pair together by lot or remain over, and show
how their turns come in natural order. Another mode of amusing them is to distribute
vessels, sometimes of gold, brass, silver, and the
like, intermixed with one another, sometimes
of one metal only; as I was saying they adapt
to their amusement the number in common use,
and in this way make more intelligible to their
pupils the arrangements and movements of
armies and expeditions, and in the management
of a household they make people more useful
to themselves, and more wide awake; and again
in measurements of things which have length,
and breadth, and depth, they free us from that
natural ignorance of all these things which is so
ludicrous and disgraceful."

The language is quaint, the games are those of a past age, but the idea embraces substantially all that we call modern in "motivation" and in "recreational methods" at the present time.

We also find the discovery frequently made anew that children should elect the subjects of their choice, having the same freedom in this respect that their elders claim. It is interesting to see the enthusiasm of the advocates of such theories, and then to read the words which Plato puts into the mouth of Protagoras: [23]

"If Hippocrates comes to me he will not experience the sort of drudgery with which other Sophists are in the habit of insulting their pupils; who, when they have just escaped from the arts, are taken and driven back into them by these teachers, and made to learn calculation, and astronomy, and geometry, and music (he gave a look at Hippias as he said this); but if he comes to me, he will learn that which he comes to learn."

IV. CONCLUSION

Summary. If it should be thought, in reading these pages, that undue emphasis has been laid upon the contributions of Greece to the pure mathematics of modern times, or of Rome to the applied mathematics, let the reader consider for a moment wherein any claim has been advanced that is not justified by the facts. It is quite possible that our indebtedness in matters of notation and symbols is not great, and this should be frankly admitted. But certain it is that no other people of the ancient world contributed to the science of demonstration in matters mathematical as did the Greeks; indeed, what nation of modern times has created (not merely extended) such great disciplines as demonstrative geometry, mathematical mechanics, algebra, trigonometry, geodesy, mathematical astronomy, theory of numbers, proportion as an instrument of research, and music as a branch of mathematics? Or taking our great mathematical discoveries, what one of these would have been made without building upon the foundations laid at Miletus, at Crotona, at Alexandria, at Perga, or in other cities or territories dominated by Greek influence?

In mathematics as applied to mechanics, what names in all the ages rank higher than Archimedes and Heron? Considering the status of the subject in their time, what names rank so high in astronomy as Hipparchus, Aristarchus, and Ptolemy? In engineering, Egypt built with brute force, but where in ancient times do we find utilitarian mathematics brought into the solution of problems as in the buildings of the Roman civilization? If we look to mathematical proportion in matters of art, what city in the world, before or since the time of Pericles, has ever ranked with Athens?

It does not seem out of place, therefore, to say that one can hardly appreciate the genesis of mathematics without a study of the works of the Greeks. Nor can one appreciate the full significance of the work of the Italians in the period of the Renaissance, in mathematics as well as in the fine arts, without knowing the relation of this work to that of the Hellenic civilization, — in particular to that of Euclid, Apollonius, Archimedes, and Diophantus. Without at least some slight knowledge of the languages of Greece and Rome, the vocabulary of mathematics, like that of most of the other sciences, is merely a mass of unmeaning terms; but with this knowledge it is a fascinating, almost poetic story.

It is difficult to say who is the greatest mathematician who ever lived; it is like asking the name of the greatest statesman or the most beautiful woman. It depends upon our definition of terms, — of the meaning of "greatest" and of "mathematician." It depends, also, upon the weight that we are to give to the state of knowledge in the lifetime of the individual. Newton was great, and so was Gauss, and so were Leibniz and Fermat. But, all things considered, what mathematician so well deserves to be called great, or even the greatest, as Archimedes? If a rival were to be named, would it not be Pythagoras?

Who, in all the world, was the greatest expositor of mathematics? Not Fermat, great genius that he was, for he wrote no work that served to make his method known. Not Leibniz, for he left no expository treatise that stands out as a classic in his field. Nor was it Pascal, or Desargues, or any one of that brilliant constellation of geniuses that characterized the France of the seventeenth and the eighteenth centuries. If one should name *La Géométrie* of Descartes, he would name a great work, but a poor piece of exposition. Indeed, when all the list has been scanned with care, what treatises will be found that in any way approach the works of Euclid and of Apollonius?

To whom do we owe primarily the logic which is the corner stone of our mathematics? To Professor Whitehead? He is a great writer and a clear thinker. To Boole, or Bertrand Russell, or De Morgan? These men were all worthy contributors. But after we examine each of the names upon the roll, must we not, after all, come back to Plato, who set the standards, and to Aristotle, who first laid out the theory?

Our study of optics (perspective) began in Greece and was carried to a higher degree of perfection in the works of the Latin writers. We have seen the subject advance to heights unsuspected by the ancient world. But even so, when we search for the origins, we look to Athens' and to Rome.

We view with satisfaction the world's advance in the theory of numbers, but is this advance commensurate, all the circumstances being considered, with that made from the time of Pythagoras to the time of Theon of Smyrna?

And if it be true, as surely seems to be the case, that this science which is interlaced with all the sciences of the present day, — indeed, which may be said to make them sciences, and which is so closely joined to every commercial and industrial and economic activity, — if it be true that this science has its beginnings, in all of its branches, in Greek or Roman soil, and there first developed into a great system, how can we who cultivate it, and who spend our years in searching out its mysteries, neglect the wisdom and the inspiration that come from a study of those brilliant *fontes et origines* which lie in the Greek and Latin literature?

[164]

NOTES AND BIBLIOGRAPHY

NOTES

[1] *Tusculan Disputations*, I. 2. 5. (Translation by C. D. Yonge, New York, 1877).

[2] *Philebus*, 56.

[3] *Tusculan Disputations*, V. 23. 64. (Translation by C. D. Yonge, with changes).

[4] Sir Thomas Heath, *A History of Greek Mathematics*, Oxford, 1921; I. 48.

[5] *Sat.*, IX. 40 ff. (Translation by Lewis Evans, New York, 1890).

[6] *Natural History*, XXXVI, Chapter 67. (Translation by Bostock and Riley, London, 1857).

[7] *Saturnalia*, I. 9. 10.

[8] *Sat.*, X. 248–9.

[9] VII. 26; IX. 30.

[10] *Commentariorum Libri IIII*. (Ed. Barocius), Padua, 1560, p. 39. (Translation by Sir Thomas Heath).

[11] G. J. Allman, *Greek Geometry from Thales to Euclid*, Dublin, 1889, p. 92.

[12] *Ibid.*, p. 16.

[13] Diophantus, *Arithmetica*, II. 11, and III. 6. (Translation by Sir Thomas Heath, 1910).

[14] *Ibid.*, VI. 19.

[15] Cf. *Opera Omnia*, Paris, 1862; I. 689.

[16] *A Description of the Admirable Table of Logarithmes*. (Wright translation, London, 1616, pp. 4, 5).

[17] Richard Dedekind, *Essays on the Theory of Numbers*. (Translated by W. W. Beman, Chicago, 1901).

[18] Sir Thomas Heath, *Apollonius of Perga*, Cambridge, 1896, p. cxviii.

[19] *Posterior Analytics*, Chapter V. (Owen translation, 1853; I. 257).

[20] *Ground of Artes*, London, c. 1542. (1558 edition, fol. A, 7. v).

[21] *Republic*, VII. 527. (Jowett translation, III. 229).

[22] *Laws*, VII. 819. (Jowett translation, V. 202).

[23] *Protagoras*, 318. (Jowett translation, I. 140).

BIBLIOGRAPHY

ALLMAN, G. J., *Greek Geometry from Thales to Euclid.* Dublin, 1889.

CANTOR, MORITZ, *Vorlesungen über Geschichte der Mathematik.* 4 vols. Leipzig, 1880–1908.

DICKSON, L. E., *History of the Theory of Numbers.* 2 vols. Washington, 1919, 1921.

GOW, JAMES, *A Short History of Greek Mathematics.* Cambridge, England, 1884.

HANKEL, HERMANN, *Zur Geschichte der Mathematik in Alterthum und Mittelalter.* Leipzig, 1874.

HEATH, SIR THOMAS LITTLE, *Euclid in Greek.* Book I. Cambridge, England, 1920.

HEATH, SIR THOMAS LITTLE, *The Thirteen Books of Euclid's Elements.* Translated from the text of Heiberg. 3 vols. Cambridge, England, 1908.

HEATH, SIR THOMAS LITTLE, *Greek Mathematics and Science.* Cambridge, England, 1921. (A pamphlet.)

HEATH, SIR THOMAS LITTLE, *A History of Greek Mathematics.* 2 vols. Oxford, 1921.

LACHMANN, K., AND RUDORFF, A., *Gromatici Veteres.* Berlin, 1848.

SMITH, DAVID EUGENE, *History of Mathematics.* 2 vols. Boston, 1923.

SMITH, SIR WILLIAM, *Dictionary of Greek and Roman Biography.* 3 vols. London, 1862–1864.

TANNERY, P., *Mémoires Scientifiques.* 2 vols. Paris, 1912. Edited by J. L. Heiberg and H. G. Zeuthen.

INDEX

INDEX

[171]

INDEX

INDEX

INDEX

INDEX

Our Debt to Greece and Rome

AUTHORS AND TITLES

AUTHORS AND TITLES

HOMER. *John A. Scott.*

SAPPHO. *David M. Robinson.*

EURIPIDES. *F. L. Lucas.*

ARISTOPHANES. *Louis E. Lord.*

DEMOSTHENES. *Charles D. Adams.*

THE POETICS OF ARISTOTLE. *Lane Cooper.*

GREEK RHETORIC AND LITERARY CRITICISM. *W. Rhys Roberts.*

LUCIAN. *Francis G. Allinson.*

CICERO AND HIS INFLUENCE. *John C. Rolfe.*

CATULLUS. *Karl P. Harrington.*

LUCRETIUS AND HIS INFLUENCE. *George Depue Hadzsits.*

OVID. *Edward Kennard Rand.*

HORACE. *Grant Showerman.*

VIRGIL. *John William Mackail.*

SENECA THE PHILOSOPHER. *Richard Mott Gummere.*

APULEIUS. *Elizabeth Hazelton Haight.*

MARTIAL. *Paul Nixon.*

PLATONISM. *Alfred Edward Taylor.*

ARISTOTELIANISM. *John L. Stocks.*

STOICISM. *Robert Mark Wenley.*

LANGUAGE AND PHILOLOGY. *Roland G. Kent.*

AUTHORS AND TITLES